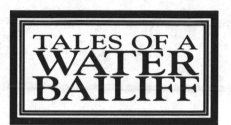

TALES OF A WATER BAILIFF

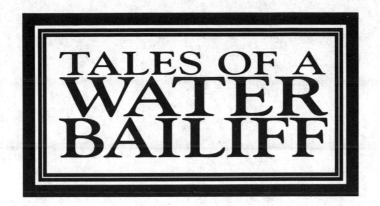

TALES OF A WATER BAILIFF

BOB DAVISON

SWAN·HILL
PRESS

Copyright © 1995 by Bob Davison (Text)
Brian Steffens (Illustrations)

First published in the UK in 1995 by Swan Hill Press,
an imprint of Airlife Publishing Ltd

British Library Cataloguing in Publication Data
A catalogue record for this book
is available from the British Library

ISBN 1 85310 528 7

Typeset by Hewer Text Composition Services, Edinburgh
Printed in England by Livesey Ltd, Shrewsbury

Swan Hill Press
an imprint of Airlife Publishing Ltd
101 Longden Road, Shrewsbury SY3 9EB

To the girls
Phyllis, Barbara, Beth, Lorraine, Alexandra.
Whose love and devotion have enhanced my life.

Acknowledgments

Robin Peardon: Brian Letts:
Malcolm Chudley: David French.
The true men of the rivers
'The Moretonhampstead Mafia'

Contents

Foreword

Several years ago, I was delighted to contribute a few words of preamble to introduce, to his fortunate readers, my old friend and colleague Bob Davison and his first book entitled *Rainbows in the Water*. Bob had then just recently retired from his job as a water bailiff with South West Water and had written a delightfully entertaining book – which you should read if you haven't already done so.

At the end of that foreword I wrote, 'I hope Bob will write a sequel before long!' Well, now he has done so and our waiting is over. *Tales of a Water Bailiff* is just what it says it is: Bob is again on his 'patch' – the glorious lakes and streams of Devon – with as rich a mix of odd characters, weird happenings and wildlife insights as you could wish to meet in many a day. This is a jolly, funny book which will have you smiling, chuckling or laughing out loud, depending upon your mood and how hard you are to please. Despite yourself, it may also touch you with a little sadness. For sure, more than once, it will give you a cold shiver even on a warm, bright day. You don't have to know fish or fishing to enjoy this book – if you are alive and human you should love it.

All his readers will, I am sure, join me in asking Bob to dig deep again for yet more tales and another sequel as soon as he can manage it.

Gordon H. Bielby
Regional General Manager
National Rivers Authority, South West Region

1

First Encounter

When I was appointed water bailiff, my 'patch' was to be three large, picturesque lakes on the eastern edge of Dartmoor. An area of intense rural beauty and tranquillity, the waters are surrounded by deep woodlands with a diversity of wildlife. Apart from a few minor law-benders the duties were pleasant, quiet and very rewarding, and I looked forward with pleasure to peaceful years until my retirement – but then I had not the remotest idea of what to expect from the other side of the coin, as it were: a bailiff's other duties. On one superb day in September I was soon to find out.

A telephone message from the head bailiff instructed me to go to a place called Dartmeet, on Dartmoor, to meet a river bailiff named Robbie, who would be waiting for me. After consulting the Ordnance map I was certain I could make the rendezvous by noon, and I left totally unprepared for what was to follow. In my ignorance, I had scorned my wife's suggestion of taking with me a flask and sandwiches, not wishing to be encumbered.

The drive across the moor was bewitching, full of interest and wonder: the vast expanse of wilderness, inhabited by tough-looking cattle, ever-chewing sheep and cocky, sturdy ponies, enthralled me. My mind was full of boyhood fantasies of Dartmoor which until now I had only experienced in books – now I was actually driving over it alone!

After three-quarters-of-an-hour's drive I arrived at the foot of the winding hill, where I could see a sparkling ribbon of water probing the rock-littered bed of the river Dart. Several cars were parked on the cinder-covered square facing an ancient clapper bridge. Late holidaymakers wandered aimlessly along the river's edge; small children threw pebbles

11

into the water, encouraging barking dogs to fetch, while elderly folk sat quietly watching and snoozing in the warm sun. I had never met the bailiff before so I concentrated on the vehicles, looking for an official radio aerial – it was much simpler in those days before the rash of CB aerials and the 'come on in' jargon that now swamps the air.

Within minutes of my parking, a car turned in from the main highway, a single pole midway along its roof. As I moved forward towards the now stationary car, a young, thin, wiry-looking fellow dressed in a Barbour coat and green wellington boots slid out of· the driver's seat, questioning my name.

'Bob – Bob Davison?'

'Yes, how are you – Robbie isn't it?' I asked, looking into a lean and hungry face in which two deep, dark rings supported a pair of oyster-like eyes. My first reaction was that this man must be suffering from a prince of hangovers – or something. His friendly country burr uncannily answered my thoughts.

'Jesus – I've been on the rake with this 'ere continental bird last night – she sure was some maid!' He spoke with such candour despite the fact we were virtual strangers. 'Did you bring a flask and some grub with you boiy?' he enquired. My negative answer seemed to disappoint him. 'Never mind, us'll find something – don't you mind.'

We locked our vehicles and, with our personal radios, set off downstream, leaving the visitors behind and gradually entering a wonderland of incredible wild beauty.

At certain stretches the river flowed at speed, carrying flotsam of herbage and empty cans that thoughtless people had discarded at the beauty spot. As it meandered and the flow slackened to a quiet surge, it was possible to hear the song of the birds, especially the skylark, who sang in frenzied non-stop bursts from high above us. A flash of colour – the kingfisher sped at breakneck speed inches from the surface of the water, scattering pockets of dancing gnats, while a couple of moorhens fled at our approach. Now the heavy breathing of my companion caused me to stop and enquire if I should slacken my pace.

'Bugger me boiy – us'll be all right – I'm hungry though!'

A further ten minutes brought us to a picture-book glade of lush green grass, smothered in an array of wild flowers. I marvelled at the sheer fairy-tale quality of the scene, fully expecting to be told that this was indeed the home of the Dartmoor pixies.

'Now listen Bob, us'll pick some mushrooms – only the small buttons mind – they big 'uns will give 'ee worms.'

I searched one half of the glade while Robbie took the other, and between us we managed to pick a pound.

'Now us'll pick some blackberries,' Robbie urged, making

for a mass of tangled briars that created a formidable barrier on one side of the meadow.

I began to wonder about the so-called poachers that we had come to watch for, but this Dartmoor man with the baggy optics knew exactly what he was about. The assortment of edibles was washed in the river before climbing the steep, rock-strewn hillside to our observation point.

Robbie spread the mushrooms and blackberries out on his jacket with a terse invitation to 'fill yer boots!' He himself tucked into mouthfuls of fungus garnished with blackberries with undisguised relish. I joined in, feigning enjoyment and remarking hypocritically, 'Delicious.' I wasn't in the least hungry, but equally had no desire to offend this man who was obviously teaching me a lesson in survival on Dartmoor. His hunger satisfied, Robbie wiped his mouth on the sleeve of his shirt, burped and exclaimed, 'They were some 'andsome!'

We both settled ourselves comfortably as possible behind the largest of boulders and waited. It surprised me how inquisitive the wild birds were: first a pert robin settled by us, waiting expectantly, but seeing nothing was on offer it soon flew off. Seconds later a pair of wagtails pitched on a nearby rock for a brief moment, but the boldest of all was a robust-looking chaffinch that actually landed not a yard from Robbie's arm, dancing in little circles as though expecting a reward for the display.

'Them's proper, they be,' he remarked tenderly, reaching for a fat berry to throw to it, but the sudden movement sent the bird off downstream.

In the distance I could hear the evocative call of the curlew, its plaintive notes accentuating the wildness of the moor, and my thoughts turned to the Stone Age men who roamed these very hills long ago. I was deep in my reverie when Robbie cocked his eyes towards the sky. 'Sun's reaching the line – them buggers will soon be here if they're coming, otherwise they won't see the fish,' he remarked wisely.

He seemed to be having trouble with his leg, for he began to scratch at the offending limb with vigour. A couple of minutes of this exercise brought relief, judging by the look on his face. 'Nothing like a good scratch to chase away they varmits,' he murmured. I thought it imprudent to enquire as to what 'they varmits' might be!

Our view of the river from the lookout spot extended for about one-and-a-half miles; here the river snaked through an acre of woodland, scrub and rocks. All was quiet except for the countless birds that chased each other, criss-crossing the river in singing play. The marked silence was broken by my companion, who pondered, 'I've been thinking boiy – you cross over to the other side of the river, just over there,' and he pointed to a spot where the water was much shallower, 'and hide yourself among they bushes.'

I looked at the spot he had pointed to and thought that this was going to be the first time I had forded a river since the war – I had better try and put on a brave face. Buttoning my Barbour, I slid awkwardly down the slope, sending showers of small stones down to the water. 'Jesus – don't make such a rattle!' he called out roughly. I reached the bank, followed by the remnants of falling stones, and looked back at him; he held up a long thumb, motioning me to cross quickly.

The river looked so much deeper now that I was alongside, and I began warily to scramble over the slippery rocks. I remembered something I had read years ago about the Dart claiming one life a year – I was determined it wasn't going to be mine. As I approached the other bank I began to feel not only relieved but downright cocky, and I attempted to jump the last remaining few feet.

Inevitably, I misjudged the distance, falling into the cold water up to my waist. I never felt the cold of the swirling water: I was too concerned over my stupidity, especially as my every movement was being monitored by the experienced moorman. Standing on the bank, the water drained down my legs into small pools at my feet and my sea-boots were full to the tops. I felt a proper twit as I emptied them of peaty water, though luckily my radio and field glasses remained dry. I sneaked a look up at Robbie, whom I could see shaking his head and mouthing obscenities at this London bloke playing at bailiff. However, I took refuge behind some gorse, about fifty yards from the holding pool, and began a miserable wet lookout.

I was now becoming hungry and longed for a hot drink.

It was about twenty minutes later when I saw three men with a lurcher dog in tow approaching downstream. On radioing my colleague, he replied drily, 'I've seen 'um – keep still!' The first man, whom I judged to be about thirty, was huge, at least seventeen stone, with dark hair and a wild, Mexican-type moustache. His head was like a beer-barrel, body like a petrol pump, with hands that could be likened to power shovels – obviously the muscle man. The second to come into view was a youngster, in his teens, unkempt, blond and as thin as a rat-catcher's dog. Last of all, also in his teens, was a softer, gentle fellow of medium height with a mass of black curly hair. His build was one of a professional dancer; he was, I learned later, the greenhorn of the trio, a makee learnee poacher.

Number two was the one with the expertise; armed with a wire snare, he knelt down over the water and watched – he obviously knew where the salmon were holed up. The third man acted as lookout, while the man-mountain was the poker. By now I had forgotten my discomfort, becoming tense, ready for battle: it was the first occasion I had felt this since the war, when, before going into action, I had experienced the same feeling. My heart thumped, blood pumping visibly in my neck.

A radio message informed my inexperienced eyes that the men had already captured two salmon. I hadn't noticed, although my eyes had never left them. I certainly had a lot to learn and was indeed thankful the moorman was with me. Suddenly, the big man slipped off the rock from which he was probing, and fell into the surging water. A non-stop flow of unhallowed verse echoed through the Dartmoor air; the greenhorn sniggered, which encouraged the man to direct abuse at the 'curly-haired git!' By this time Robbie had used the diversion to leave his hideout; I never saw him leave. Over the RT he informed me he was looking for their vehicle. 'I've got an idea where it will be too – just keep me informed of their movements. Four zero out!'

I decided that if the poachers moved towards me I would at least take one of them. However, it wasn't long before my colleague radioed, 'Found the car, know who they are, especially the big 'un. I'm going for my car; radio the minute

16

they leave and join me at the wall near the bridge -out!' It seemed that he had located the poachers' vehicle not three hundred yards from his own.

Ten minutes later the trio decided to leave, quickly turning upstream towards the bridge. I could make out that one of them carried a plastic sack which no doubt contained the fish. Muscle man was still cursing about his ducking as they hurried along the bank; the lurcher plodded happily behind the trio, cocking his leg every ten yards or so. I followed in the same way I had seen a private eye shadow a suspect on TV and felt I was acting out, if not laughably, an important role here on Dartmoor. In fact, I enjoyed the cops and robbers until, in my eagerness, I stumbled over a rock, badly grazing my shin. But I didn't feel the pain – just a desire not to let the men out of my sight.

Pulling myself to my feet, I noticed that my quarry was out of sight , and I hurried quickly towards the bridge. I swear a couple of ducks were laughing at me as I scrambled through the gorse and bracken; never mind, I was determined to prove that I had the makings of an efficient water bailiff. The ducks took off in noisy alarm as, stupidly, I threw a twig at them: the noise of the flight could have warned the poachers that somebody was about.

Although I still hadn't caught sight of the three, I could hear raised voices and a squeal of brakes through my radio, which Robbie had left open – on purpose, no doubt, for my benefit. I radioed quickly that I was within earshot, but received no answer. I ran the remaining distance, and saw that Robbie had positioned his car immediately in front of the offenders' vehicle and had jumped out to grab the youngest of the trio, who was attempting to reverse his car. The wheels spun, unable to grip the wet grass, and the RT came alive, urging me to close with the suspects. Breathlessly I answered that I could now see them: the muscle man was threatening the bailiff to get him to release the driver.

Much to my relieved surprise, my sudden appearance subdued him; the greyness of my beard must have stirred some hidden memory of his headmaster, as I attempted with as much authority as I could muster to ease the confrontation.

To Robbie's delight, I spoke into my radio to fictitious reinforcements, saying out loud, 'No further assistance needed for the moment, suspects attempting no violence, stay in position. Three eight out!' It did the trick, thank God! Man-mountain alone could have massacred us both. The three accepted defeat with no more than obscenities.

After the usual procedure of confiscating the fish and tackle, and the recording of copious notes, we sent them on their dispirited way. I looked at Robbie with relief: the time was half-past six and I longed for a refreshing drink, feeling pleased with my very first encounter with poachers.

'You're some clever, Bob, the message about reinforcements did sure fool 'em; you'm not so dumb after all.' I had no idea that he thought I was dumb in the first place, but I shrugged off the unintended insult and quickly suggested a drink. Once again my mate said, 'Bugger me Bob – I'm 'ungry!'

After driving two miles from the incident, we parked in a lay-by. It was deserted and silent.

'Hang on a minute, I'll not be long,' Robbie said, taking a twelve-bore gun from the boot of his car. 'I know the farmer here, went to school together; just 'ang on 'ere a minute boiy.' With that he vanished over the high hedge of a nearby field. I honestly had no idea what he intended to do.

It was now becoming chilly, the previous ducking I had was taking effect, and a burning sensation down my leg revealed an angry-looking weal from the fall I had received earlier on. Two loud reports from the field made me forget my discomfort. Perhaps, I thought, he has seen the poachers again and has taken a pot-shot at them – surely that's a bit much? I was confused.

Robbie emerged grinning, holding up two limp rabbits. I just couldn't believe it – perhaps they were for his dinner.

'Us'll be all right boiy,' he said, tossing the warm bodies on the back seat of his car. Without another word he motioned me to follow as he drove off, eventually stopping outside a tiny pub that sat in isolated splendour in the valley. Once again I was told to 'hang on' as he entered the hostelry. Now what, I wondered? Out he came, carrying a large bottle of cider which he held up for my inspection saying, 'This be proper,' as he climbed into his car, waving his arm for me to follow.

We drove to high ground through uncharted land until we reached a spot with breathtaking views.

'Bob, you'm going to see a sunset you'm never see'd before,' he remarked, tossing the brace of rabbits for me to carry. By now I had begun to enter into this unexpected bonus of an adventure. As we walked, I noticed that he stopped to pick at some green vegetation, gathering a few sprigs as we made for a clearing on the rocky hillside.

The skyline was now ablaze in orange splendour; it was very inspiring, so much so that I became quite emotional, wishing that I could play some Debussy right there and then on this enchanting spot.

'Proper – 'eh boiy?' Robbie began preparing a small fire, collecting some loose rocks to frame the crackling wood.

I marvelled at the matter-of-fact way in which he systematically went about the chore of preparing the rabbits: from the boot of the car he took some wrinkled tinfoil, in which he wrapped the skinned bodies with green vegetation.

'What's that stuff?' I asked, puzzled. He grinned slyly before answering.

'Don't 'ee know what that be? Wild garlic boiy – 'andsome!'

The expertise with which he cooked the warm flesh impressed – the aroma of the cooking and the pungent scent of the fire up here, overlooking the blazing sky, will remain with me until I die. The distant, brief call of a pheasant completed the scene to perfection.

We washed down the impromptu meal with tangy cider, and at last I began to feel I had arrived. Dartmoor, with all her mystery and grandeur, seemed encapsulated in this simple but magnificent banquet.

Hunger satisfied, we both lay wrapped in our Barbours looking at the night sky. Time didn't seem to matter. I honestly could have stayed all night, silently observing the planets in the dying embers of the fire.

2

The Reporter

It is surprising how recently the poaching of salmon has invaded the headlines of our national and local newspapers. Of course, it is common knowledge that poaching has existed ever since man learned how to steal, and in times past it was often deemed justified in order that the unfortunate peasants survive in what was then a hard and cruel society. Although times have indeed changed and we are living in a welfare state where nobody need starve, nevertheless, age-old avarice is always present. The uncontrollable urge to make a 'quick buck' has become more prevalent in today's materialistic age of hi-fi, computers and Costa holidays. At last, thank goodness, the law is becoming more aware of the seriousness of poaching and the attendant violence that occurs with alarming frequency. Some organised gangs make as much as a thousand pounds per week, tax free – much more during the seasonal salmon runs, when they will resort to any sort of violence in order to avoid detention. Many instances of brutal force and bodily harm have been recorded in England, Scotland and Wales – in fact wherever fertile rivers flow.

What's more – it's on the increase!

A popular national newspaper had repeatedly asked the authorities if a reporter might be permitted to accompany water bailiffs on one of their anti-poaching patrols (APPs). Understandably, the powers-that-be were reluctant to have their *modus operandi* made known to the public, as this information would, of course, have been invaluable to the thieves. However, after consultations with fisheries officers it was agreed that a reporter would be present during a routine APP. It was stressed that he was to hold himself in readiness at short notice and should present himself suitably dressed for a taxing, uncomfortable and probably damp session. The editor responded readily to the invitation, promising that a reporter would be available.

July came and went, with an excellent run of peal (sea-trout) in all rivers in the south-west. The waters managed to maintain a reasonably high flow, enabling the migratory fish to reach the spawning beds, and the water bailiffs had been kept busy with the usual outbreaks of poaching. There had been some successes, and of course the inevitable failures, but on the whole it hadn't been all that bad. However, with the forthcoming run of autumn salmon the story would be completely different, and most certainly hazardous.

Our tale begins in late September on the river Teign, which flows through some of the most picturesque and dramatic countryside in the area. Poachers refer to certain stretches of this fertile river as their 'piggy-bank'. Robin the river bailiff was on the last mile of his foot patrol; it was four-thirty in the afternoon with a sky that threatened rain, he was hungry and thirsty, and his legs ached after a six-mile walk. He looked forward to his regular 'Buffs' meeting in the evening, when he could relax and enjoy a drink with his friends. The head bailiff, who lived in the same village, would also be there, and was not averse to a drop of fluid before it all disappeared.

At a quarter to five, with only a short distance left before completing his 'beat', quite by chance Robin discovered a net strung across a river. It was cleverly set and camouflaged, although admittedly it was in a productive, deep pool where you expect to find one. Robin, who was in urgent need of a private place in which to relieve himself, wandered off the narrow track into the dense undergrowth of the bank, screened by formidable brambles. In order to secure strict privacy, he made a forced entry through the foliage where, breathing a sigh of welcome relief, he stood surveying the river. Suddenly, his eyes were alerted by the glint of the scales of a freshly run salmon caught in the net.

The reporter, whom I shall call Clarence, was the only available man the editor could call on in a hurry. Young, twenty-plus, lean and tall with a pale, serious-looking face, his large, black-rimmed spectacles gave him a look of academic learning, and every so often he would give nervous little coughs in the manner of a waiter expectantly awaiting a tip.

Clarence arrived at the boat store dressed from head to toe in bright yellow oilskins, looking for all the world like a gigantic, misshapen banana. The head bailiff (HB) exploded when he saw this yellow apparition, telling him that such apparel would be suicide and was totally unsuitable.

'Oh dear' – cough, cough – he murmured, as he was led away to be rigged out in camouflage clothing. The

transformation was dramatic. As he viewed himself in the mirror Clarence enthused, 'I say – this is great!' And he gave the air an elaborate karate chop. As the bailiffs checked radios and various items of equipment, Clarence wrote furiously in his notebook, looking up every so often to smile at all and sundry.

Outside the rain had begun to fall, steadily at first and then in solid sheets, bouncing up from the concrete slipway of the boathouse in tiny fountains.

'Christ – that's all we want! Right lads, get everything into the Land Rover and we'll poodle off. By the way . . . ' the head man turned to the reporter, 'what do they call you?'

'Clary.'

'OK Clary – no smoking, keep quiet, and when the dirt hits the fan – keep well out of the way!'

Robin quickly contacted the head bailiff, who immediately set the necessary operation in motion and instructed him to remain with the net until the main party arrived. Robin was an old hand at the game and derived satisfaction from deterring these robbers of the river. His twenty years of service had brought him into contact with many villains, and a reputation throughout the county which gained him respect and, needless to say loathing, among the small-time opportunist poachers. But unknown to him, this time his discovery was to confront him with the notorious gang from up country.

Suitably dressed for a long wait, especially as the sky was beginning to cloud over, threatening rain, Robin smoked a last cigarette in the comfort of his car before driving to a nearby cover of trees to conceal his vehicle. Satisfied that it was well hidden from the main highway, he retraced his footsteps back to the net, wishing he had brought a spare flask. He knew from experience that although he had his cigarettes as comfort, it would have been extremely unwise to smoke once he was *in situ*, as the scent of tobacco could be detected from quite a distance. Many a poacher has, in fact, betrayed his presence by the acrid smell of a cigarette in the virgin moorland air.

Carefully selecting a suitable vantage point, Robin settled himself bang in the middle of a mixture of gorse, brambles and aromatic honeysuckle, and reflected on his last outing with his young lady. Meanwhile, back at HQ, telephones rang busily, summoning bailiffs and one newspaper reporter, informing them of the task and its urgency.

The head bailiff joined the others in the Land Rover and the party splashed off to the river. It had now become chilly in the fading light and the vehicle was well and truly hidden as it travelled to the scene. A muted message to Robin telling him of the arrival was received with relief; doubly so as, so far, the area was clear of any suspects. Two bailiffs were detailed to take up their station on the opposite bank, while the remainder proceeded to join Robin. Clarence stayed close to HB, and was beginning to show mild signs of apprehension as they were swallowed up by the intense darkness of the riverside. His nervous attempts at conversation were cut short by HB, who held up his hand to his mouth and hissed for complete silence.

In torrential rain they picked their way along the bank, occasionally stumbling over the exposed roots that veined the scoured bankside. The rain had by now begun to filter down the reporter's neck, causing him at first mild discomfort, which showed plainly on his death-white face. By the time they had reached the rendezvous he was displaying open irritation, especially at the frequent need to wipe his steamed-up glasses. Like a Dutch uncle, HB found a partially sheltered spot in the nearby herbage for Clarence, stressing that on no account was he to move unless directed.

Clarence squatted down in the middle of the dripping branches and prickly brambles; his innocent child-like face looked up as he quietly thanked the gruff, no-nonsense head man. The long, cold wait began, in total darkness, with the rain falling steadily. The flurry of a disturbed wood pigeon set the reporter's heart racing, as the sound of flapping wings was magnified in the night air.

HB had positioned himself some thirty yards from the reporter so that, armed with a night-sight, he had a commanding view of the rogue net. After twenty minutes or so the rain began to ease and HB was alerted by the clumsy footsteps coming towards him. He felt the adrenalin begin to flow; resisting the natural urge to contact his colleagues, he then saw approaching through the sodden bushes the white, bespectacled face of Clarence.

'What's the matter?' hissed HB, plainly annoyed.

'Please, I want to go to the lavatory,' pleaded the reporter like a bewildered schoolboy, 'I can't wait!'

'There's no bloody toilets out here – find yourself a spot – but for Christ's sake keep hidden or you'll blow the whole operation!' HB delivered the advice with ill-concealed anger, looking towards the sky as though seeking help from above.

'Yes – thank you, I'll be careful – thank you.' The soft tones of a little boy lost faded as Clarence returned to the darkness. From the distant bushes the discreet sound of the nervous cough could be heard, conjuring up all manner of things for HB who shook his head, muttering 'Jesus Christ!'

Clarence's eventual return to his hiding place was signalled as he barged through the dripping branches by a distinct 'Oh bother!' And he became silent once more. Mercifully the rain had stopped; the steady plop, plop of the soaking vegetation accompanied the distant sound of the river slurping over the weir. Breaks in the cloud showed there was a moon somewhere wanting to shine. Clarence took comfort from the brief glimpses of moonlight, for he was unutterably miserable and cold, and wished to God he was tucked up warmly in bed. His clothing had become disarranged during the emergency, the continual drips from the leaves had found a spot of exposed flesh at his waist, causing him to loose his cool, and he used a very rude word loudly to relieve himself of the frustration.

Within seconds of Robin's radio message, HB also saw the pale underbellies of the fish floating downstream on their sides towards the net. This was an extremely vicious and disgusting method of poaching: the river was being poisoned further upstream, just sufficiently to deprive the salmon of oxygen, but nevertheless spelling certain annihilation for next season's fish. Thousands of fry and parr destroyed in one fell swoop – perpetrated by man's obsessive greed and complete disregard for all the wildlife in the river.

The head bailiff seethed with anger, making him all the more determined to bring these monsters to justice. Clarence sensed something was afoot; he had heard the crackling of the radio and was beginning to feel a strange stirring in his stomach, and thought, 'God – this is it!' He strained his eyes into the semi-darkness of the clearing to see if the bailiffs were making a move; all was silent.

Somewhere out there he could smell smoke – tobacco smoke. He wanted to shout aloud to HB, but feared his wrath. Three men came hurrying down the river; one was actually smoking, showing utter disregard of any caution, as they began to bag the stunned fish. In fact, the men made no attempt to minimise the noise as they commented laughingly to one another on the magnificence of the haul. There were at least ten salmon being stowed in plastic bags. Then, as the net was being released by one of the poachers, the bailiffs broke cover.

After the initial shock and surprise, all hell broke loose, and one poacher was immediately detained and handcuffed. Meanwhile the other two fought like tigers with their hands, feet and even their mouths, while the rain-drenched valley echoed to the cursing and oaths. After a spirited struggle two of them were finally in custody and suitably subdued, while the remaining one ran off.

Now I must be fair: Clarence had been so shocked at the sheer fury of the encounter that he had crouched deep in the bushes, completely mesmerised by it all, but at that moment he suddenly leapt up and attempted to block the runaway, who immediately grappled with him. Clarence was promptly picked up and thrown bodily into a robust gorse bush, as the assailant vanished into the darkness.

While the two thieves were taken to the police station, Clarence stayed behind with a bailiff to help him collect the net and fish – fourteen in all – and await the return of the others. By four o'clock the sky had cleared, with a cold easterly coming in. The reporter was in his element and, although shaken and feeling a little bruised, he wrote non-stop in his notebook. The adjectives flowed from his pen in the approaching dawn.

Finally, the bailiff asked Clarence what prompted him to tackle the thug when it was appreciated that he was, let's face it, an academic young man who would not have looked out of place behind a florist's counter.

'Oh I don't know, I suddenly thought, what the hell, I'm English – I'm not a coward – but I must confess my bum is full of prickles. You know, I'm glad I've experienced this rough and tumble, I would not have missed this for the world. My editor is going to be pleased when he reads my report.'

This was the longest speech he had made since arriving; he was definitely on a 'high' from the excitement and, no doubt, relief.

In the cold morning the eventual return of the party was greeted warmly, especially as they had brought flasks of steaming coffee and rolls back with them.

The head bailiff gave Clarence a blast for putting himself at risk, and with the next breath a thump on the back, saying roughly 'You'm proper, boiy!' The cheeks of the reporter coloured as he shuffled uneasily, and with downcast eyes he quickly replied, 'Thank you very much Malcolm.'

Later it was learned that the runaway had been detained by the police a few miles away on the motorway leading to Dorset. It was easy really – the poachers were known to the authority and to the police. They were members of a notorious gang. They were given short prison sentences, and reports say they are again active on the rivers – even as far away as Scotland!

Will we ever prevent poaching? Of course not! Only when the rivers become barren and man has actually destroyed himself will we be able to close the book on this second oldest of professions.

3

An Act of Folly

I was once asked if I could recall ever being afraid during my career as a water bailiff. Some time later, in the comfort of my armchair on a chilly November night, I embarked on a nostalgic journey covering the past years. I could recall at least two occasions when, hand on my heart, I could honestly say yes – twice, when I had experienced the same feeling as when my frigate had been hit during the last war, the difference being that this time it had happened through my own carelessness and 'familiarity breeds contempt' attitude. I choose to tell of this incident knowing full well that I am not alone in this nonchalant approach to everyday routine.

The county had been enjoying a spell of warm weather and light breezes, which encouraged the holidaymakers to flock into Devon in their thousands. Experts predicted a long, dry summer; the fields were green, the rivers and lakes full, and birds were nesting. The early flow of visitors augured well for a record season and I looked forward with immense pleasure to another spell of river and lakeside patrols.

That Friday was no different to the previous Friday: blue skies with light clouds, just a suspicion of a breeze. The newly arrived swallows were busy collecting mud from the river to house next year's brood. I began my duties by taking the patrol boat out on a flat-calm lake which reflected the shimmering landscape; here the waters were sheltered on either bank by sloping hills of pine, the haunt of many wild creatures. The warm breeze barely ruffled the downy neck feathers of the resident geese, who paddled out in convoy to receive their daily ration of stale Hovis.

I headed for the fish cages that were moored in mid-water, full of hundreds of rainbow trout. The entire surface of the

28

water boiled as the fish picked up the rhythmic beat of the screw; for they, too, were awaiting their breakfast. Three black shags lined the cage, their outstretched wings giving them a look of Gothic gargoyles as they dried themselves after a meal. They rose laboriously into the air, followed by a clumsy heron who protested noisily as it gained height, tucking its long legs into its body and heading for the north end of the waters. Trout were feeding in the lake from ever-rising nymphs, sending tiny, ever-widening circles towards the rushes where a family of frogs squatted and stared. All around me was perfection, beauty and serenity.

My next venue was altogether different: the lake was high on the moor, surrounded by scrub, gorse and rocks. A half-hour's journey found me climbing the steep, narrow road to the bleak moor where, without warning, one is confronted with a vast, open panorama of rolling hills dotted with ever-hungry sheep, indifferent ponies and surly-looking Aberdeen Angus bullocks. A gale warning had been given on the car radio as I neared the waters, but I disregarded the message as I knew I should have finished my chores by the time it arrived.

Pulling the patrol boat from the moorings, I was a little surprised to see a decided ruffling of the water, the breeze strengthening already from the west. I wasn't unduly concerned, but what did stop me in my tracks was the sight of the 'stocking boat' – a specially designed craft to hold fish, and very precious – adrift from her moorings and heading for the dam overflow, which had a drop of some sixty feet!

It had fouled the boom, a one-inch manila rope strung across the reservoir in the water, thirty feet from the drop. Against all my experience and naval training, I climbed aboard without a lifejacket: why bother with one on an inland lake – hadn't I sailed the Atlantic? I also forgot to secure my knife around my waist, a must in any craft! I reasoned that it would not take long, and decided to feed the trout first.

The heavy engine burst into life and I was off towards the cages, which by now were rolling in the increasing swell. A kingfisher was trapped in one of the nets covering the cage and it took some time to undo the complicated arrangements of nets and set it free. It flew away like a silent shot from a gun. The fish fed, some two thousand , I made for the dam; the wind now was blowing hard and shipping water over my bows.

Shutting off the engine, I floated over the boom in a following wind and quickly made fast the stocking boat to mine. I crept back towards the boom, stopped the engine and began to float nicely over the rope. Once clear I restarted the power; alas, only on the third pull. It was too late – the boat was blown back towards the manila rope, which became well and truly wrapped around the propeller. It was

absolutely impossible for me to gain any slack to loosen its vice-like grip.

I looked around for help, but the area was devoid of any human being, even though it was noon. The wind was now force eight, the waters flecked with long wind-lanes, and to make matters worse the combined weight of the two boats caused the rope-boom to belly towards the sixty-foot drop.

Although I was reluctant to let go the very craft that I had come to save, I cast off where it edged slowly towards the edge of the dam. I searched feverishly for anything I could use to cut the offending hawser and found a bunch of keys in my pocket, the biggest of which I used in an attempt to saw through the rope. After a few minutes, which seemed like an hour, I had succeeded only in removing most of the skin of my finger, which now looked like a chicken's bloody neck. The rope sported just a few displaced strands. The boat edged nearer the chasm, the wind was now screaming past my ears. I was still really more annoyed by my stupidity than frightened.

Thirty-five minutes later and with twelve feet to go, my cries were heard by the retired keeper of seventy-plus who, after a lot of signals and gestures, managed to release the boom from the shore end. I managed to land both craft and myself to safety.

A lesson well learned – but then you would think a man of my age should have known better.

Yes! I was indeed frightened!

4

Starbuck

The fishing season was drawing to a close, the hustle and bustle of holidaymakers dwindling, leaving a peaceful atmosphere on the waters – September is a magical month. Poachers had been active during the past summer, not only on the rivers but also on the inland lakes, which in their turn had felt the greedy hands of these sometimes violent predators. One of their favourite methods was to lay baited lines with multi-hooks across the water overnight – hence the term 'night-lines' – and during the early hours of morning reap their illegal harvest. It was therefore necessary for bailiffs to make early morning searches of the fishery. In my case, this covered several miles of banks in a setting of incredible beauty, where the waters were flanked on both sides by woodland, affording superb avenues of escape for the poachers. A most difficult terrain.

It was six o'clock as I began my early patrol of the Dartmoor lakes, searching for night-lines along three miles of beautiful, magical waterside. A light, wispy mist hung eerily over the water and I could hear the dull flops as the fish took the unwary fly. Canada geese were awake, sailing silently across the lake like some long-forgotten armada. Herons were already fishing, like absent-minded judges, stabbing the water as if making a point of order. My feet sank into the centuries-old moss, and I felt like an intruder on this tranquil scene. How strange, I mused, that no anglers were about at one of the most productive periods of the day. Still I enjoyed the reverie.

A half-hour's walk brought me to the bay and the first small fishing hut, where I had my morning cigarette. The hut consisted of rough planking forming a snug, box-like apartment for two which nestled into the hillside, covered in heather and dying bracken. Wild honeysuckle clambered over the entire structure, scenting the interior with permanent summer. I sat on the rough bench inside, looking out to the bay. To my right a small feeder-stream bubbled down from the oak plantation, entering the lake in a silent swirl. Here a dog-fox, magnificent ruddy brown, lapped fastidiously, his body partly hidden by the giant ferns that clustered the gravelled bed. Already brown trout were gathered in the shallows, eager to reach upstream to the spawning beds. The raucous, irritable croaking of a disturbed heron filled the air as it rose laboriously with a loud flapping of its wings, heralding the arrival of another fox who daintily greeted the other with a moist kiss.

Shafts of early morning sun pierced the larch plantation, spotlighting two argumentative squirrels disputing the ownership of a single hazelnut. All around life was stirring; through the mist blue damsel flies were beginning their puppet-like dance, watched by an elderly grass-snake as it glided from a clump of rosy campion into the water. I continued on upstream, taking deep breaths of pure moorland air, silently thanking 'above' for this wonderful life.

It was not long before I reached the extreme north end, a long, low, narrow causeway stretched across the width of the water where the main stream entered. There, partially wreathed in the cottonwool mist, stood a lone fisherman, tall and gaunt with an aristocratic bearing. On the shoulder of his Victorian fishing jacket hung an old cane creel, and he cast his fly with just the slightest movement of his wrist. How different from some of the frenzied actions I had witnessed this season – his fly landed as lightly as a snowflake. This was indeed a master at work.

I stood a little distance off to watch him. His face was expressionless; deeply etched lines furrowed his brow, and every so often he would touch his nose with an irritated movement of the hand to discourage the biting midges. He looked sad, and very wise. He took no notice of me; I offered a 'Good morning!', but was answered with a curt nod. His eyes never left the water; his rod was of cane, burnt to a deep gold by many summers.

'I cannot recall seeing you here before, sir,' I ventured.

In a soft country burr, he answered, 'I have been fishing these waters a long time laddie – I've had some good fish from this spot.'

'What is your name, sir?'

His reply was short and crisp: 'Starbuck!'

It was obvious that this was the end of the conversation as far as he was concerned. I continued my patrol, somewhat puzzled. It was only at breakfast a little later that I realised

I had not inspected his licence. What a strange effect this person had had over me during the early morning magic. I never saw him again.

It was three weeks later while having a drink with one of my oldest anglers, a man of eighty-five, that the conversation reached 'lures versus flies' – always a bone of contention with the purists – and I mentioned my encounter with the early morning fisherman. I was describing him, his method and his dress at great length when I noticed my companion's face drain.

'Impossible!' He snapped. 'What was his name, eh?' I was

surprised at the sharpness of his tone, in contrast to his normally placid nature.

'Oh yes, I could never forget that name – it had a ring to it. Starbuck.' He looked at me long and hard before answering.

'Good God man – that's impossible! He fished this lake for forty years.' The old man suddenly looked tired. In a subdued voice he continued, 'But he's been dead for well over fifty years. I was a young man at the time – 'twas a sad affair.' A far-away look came into my friend's eyes. 'We found him one morning drowned by the causeway – his favourite spot, you know. They said it was a broken heart after his wife died . . .'

I often pass this lonely spot during my patrols; although I know I shall never see Starbuck again, I somehow feel he is around . . .

5

Paddy

Paddy was the kind of person that most of us, I suspect, have known at one time or another during a lifetime. He was what is commonly known as a 'likeable rogue'. His philosophy seemed to be that any authority, laws or by-laws, although a necessary evil, were definitely made to be broken or disregarded. But of course, there has to come a time when a firm line has to be taken, regardless of the affability of the person concerned.

I would find Paddy fishing at most of the authority's fisheries, sometimes as frequently as three or four times a week, and there was no doubt at all that he was an avid fisherman regardless, apparently, of the cost, although in fact he was unemployed. In his fifties, of average height, portly, with a complexion that could match a rising sun, he was a pure nondescript except for the one endearing gift: he had a charming turn of phrase, a gift that enabled him to translate everyday common-or-garden speech into delightful, descriptive prose.

The fishing season was just three weeks old; the lakes were full of prime trout, catches were good, attendances by holidaymakers and locals excellent. It was during one of my routine patrols that I first met Paddy fishing a small, picturesque bay aptly named 'Rainbow Bay'. Approaching, I saw that he had already caught two fine fish that lay on the bank, partially covered by fronds of bracken. Announcing my identity, I was greeted with a warm smile and salutation. "Tis a fine mornin' yer 'onhour – is it my licence you be wantin'?'

I was tempted to enter into the spirit of the banter but thought better of it; after all, I thought, I should maintain that certain sense of decorum befitting a water bailiff.

His licence and permit were in order; so, having dispensed with the legal formalities, I pursued a more relaxed form of conversation. I must say, I was completely thrown by the candour of the man, who, having once started the conversation, monopolised the next fifteen minutes with tales of his life and misfortunes. It was all delivered in the soft brogue of deepest Ireland, each sentence literally brimming with shamrock and Guinness.

I learned that he hailed from the County Wicklow and had come to England five years earlier. He was a bachelor by choice and, unlike the vast majority of Irish immigrants, did not use a pick and shovel. What's more, he had no intentions of doing so. Since arriving on these shores he had held many minor jobs, among which barman predominated ('Sure, I like a wee drop of the hard before it's all gone'). Unfortunately, a brush with the law had resulted in a recent spell in prison. 'I'll tell you, 'twas a terrible old six months locked away from the fields and the birds, sor!' I felt compassion for this plain, honest-speaking man.

'Would you be having a little old cigarette to spare, sor?' he suddenly asked, wedging the request succinctly within a rather long, drawn-out narrative. The subtlety of his delivery was masterful. I gave him the remainder of a packet of twenty, which was received with a brief, "Tis a powerful man you are, sor – may your shadow never grow less.'

He continued non-stop about the injustices of the world until I was forced to cut short the soliloquy – I had other anglers to visit. Wishing him a successful day, I continued my patrol. Turning the bend of the lake, I looked back at him and found he was watching me; he waved a friendly goodbye.

During the next few weeks I was to meet him several times at fisheries all over the county, and what's more, he always had a bag full of trout. Regardless of being unemployed, he was always in possession of a current licence, and ready to produce it in an engaging, friendly manner. Moreover, regardless of adverse fishing conditions, when anglers were lucky if they managed to take home one fish Paddy always had his legal limit.

This man was obviously a good fisherman – or was he?

Paddy

I must confess that I was reluctant to harbour unpleasant thoughts about him, especially as on one cold day he kindly offered me a cup of coffee from his battered flask. Although I graciously declined, I appreciated the kind thought – he was that kind of person.

The ever-present poaching by organised gangs kept us bailiffs busy, and much night work was necessary for us to keep some semblance of control, although I must say it was difficult and still is. One early morning I had finished an observation on one known productive pool where at least two salmon were lurking; the time was a little after five, and I had been out in the field since ten the previous night. Already the sun was showing the makings of another fine day, so instead of going home for breakfast and a snooze I decided to do a quick check of the reservoir that was near my home.

I reckoned it would take me at least an hour to walk around the lake, which would at least sharpen my appetite. The morning was idyllic, a light southerly breeze barely ruffled the water and, apart from the Canada geese foraging among the reeds, all was deserted. I strode off making the first bay – Rainbow Bay – within twenty minutes. There among the clutter of granite boulders that nudged the water, I heard faint squeakings, sort of soft, immature meows. Tiptoeing on the moss that carpeted the area I saw behind a lichen-covered rock a family of young wild mink being fed with a raw trout by the parent. I was fascinated.

I retreated into the cover of hazel a little way on to the hillside to observe unseen and without fear of disturbing this enchanting early morning scene. Although mink are regarded as a pest I certainly haven't got the heart to destroy them; the sun that morning caught their coats, giving them a rippling velvet sheen. A heron pitched down on the point of the bay and studied the water with grave thoughtfulness. The entire area was ringed with rising fish as the hatch of flies began their suicidal dance over the shimmering surface. Not three feet away, an adder stretched itself out on a nearby rock to enjoy the warmth of the sun, which was now clearing the top of the larch plantation.

The raucous croak of the heron as it climbed into the sky jolted my senses – a sure sign that somebody was around. I decided to remain in the cover for a while to study the superb manoeuvres of a large dragonfly.

Coming into sight around the way was Paddy, who seemed to be gliding over the moss-covered pathway in a manner very much akin to that of a stalker – or poacher. He moved with a certain grace and stealth – definitely not the normal movement of man. Stopping in the shade of an oak that dominated the bank, he threw his bag and tackle down and began to roll a cigarette, at the same time surveying the water. He cocked an ear towards the boulders and waited, before walking towards the faint cries of the mink. Leaning over, he studied the small creatures; drawing heavily on his cigarette, he watched in silence. Suddenly, saying out loud, 'Well me little darlins, 'tis beautiful you look now – but I'm thinking 'tis a mighty lot of damage you'll be doing soon,' he returned to his tackle, taking from the fishing bag a cardboard container. My leg was now in cramp; I rubbed to restore the circulation, deciding to remain hidden a moment longer. I didn't quite know why – it was just a feeling I had. Shifting my weight on to the other leg, I waited – for what, I didn't know.

Paddy was now at the water's edge and seemed to be feeding the fish with handfuls of brown pellets; when the box was empty, he began preparing his rod for fishing. It was now evident why he always fished this particular spot. In fact, what he was doing was illegal under the Salmon & Freshwater Act: ground-baiting the area to encourage the trout to shoal. Whereas with coarse fishing this method was permissible, in no way was it allowed for game fishing: fly only or, in some cases, spinning and the odd maggot in the river, but ground-baiting – good God! Sacrilege! No wonder he always went home with a full bag.

I waited until he cast his line into the water before breaking cover. He didn't see me, for that instant his fly was taken, and so intent was he on landing the fish that he began to croon softly, 'There my little darlin', come to dada,' and I managed to reach him completely unseen. Placing my hand on his shoulder I said, 'So this is what the secret is, Paddy me lad!'

Virtually jumping out of his skin, he dropped the rod on the bank.

'Jesus mother of God! Is it me death you be wanting?'

'No – not your death Paddy, fair play. No wonder you are known as the "Purveyor of Trout"!'

'Mister bailiff, sor, I swear to God I never knew that it was illegal to feed the little old fishes, sor, 'tis mighty sorry I am yer 'onhour, my old heart is galloping away, so it is – feel it now!' He attempted to place my hand against his shirt.

I decided to take a firm line with him and for the next few minutes gave him a severe reprimand, warning him of the penalties if he was to repeat the offence in the future. Although he gave the impression of being suitably chastised,

I noticed that he had already placed a foot on his fallen rod to check the trout's escape. All the time I had been talking his eyes had never left the tell-tale jerking of his rod. My reprimand ran off his back like water. When I had finished my spirited warning he fell on his knees and, grabbing my hand, he cried, 'Merciful God, you're a fine man, sor, so you are. A prayer I'll be saying for you tonight – bless you.'

And what is more, I do believe he meant it.

I left him, knowing he was secretly laughing at me – but I could afford to wait. On reaching the office after my patrol I noticed that Paddy was the only one fishing on the lake, and also that there was only one vehicle on the dam. An Austin that had seen better days, I suspected rightly that it belonged to our Irish friend.

Trying the boot, I found it unlocked and pulled it open. What a surprise, for among an assortment of dirty sacks and tools was a residue of slime and fish scales – salmon scales. I quickly scraped up a portion of slime and scales for examination at headquarters, at the same time noting the car's registration for circulation among the bailiffs. The vehicle displayed no road tax: I must point out that this particular reservoir is situated in a remote spot of the moor, seldom patrolled as the police are up to their eyes with hoards of holidaymakers and are subsequently kept extremely busy.

The result of the examination confirmed that the scales were from a mature salmon of about ten pounds, recently caught. The policeman confirmed that the vehicle did belong to our friend with the silver tongue. From now on he was going to be kept under close observation.

That Sunday there was to be an open fishing competition at the lake. It was to start at nine in the morning, and by eight the competitors were already arriving, straining at the leash. Sure enough, Paddy arrived in his Austin, beaming to all and sundry. It was the first time I had seen him since the early morning encounter; he greeted me with the reverence of a saint as he signed the entry book.

'Good mornin' mister bailiff, sor, I'm thinking the sun's too bright, 'tis cloud we be wanting, would you be having a little old match, for haven't I gone and lost me lighter, so

I have.' Of course, I gave him a box of matches which, after lighting his discoloured weed of a cigarette, he promptly put in his pocket and left the office. I could not be bothered to ask for them; the man was not of this world.

The hooter sounded the signal for the end of the competition and the long trek back to the office began, with the anglers bringing their bags to be recorded and weighed. Many had their limit of five fish; one rod had a specimen trout of four pounds-plus and was obviously a candidate for a prize. There were still some anglers to report who had been fishing the extreme end of the waters – Paddy was one of them.

At last the remaining rods arrived, their catches duly weighed and recorded; I acted as scrutineer. Paddy would seem to be eligible for the heaviest bag, topping the others by at least a pound. Now I was puzzled, for his fish seemed no bigger than others that I had inspected. Calling him over to the table, I asked to inspect his fish again. 'Sure, sor, you have some fine trout in your waters – is that not so?' He looked around for confirmation among the fishermen.

Probing the guts of the fish, I felt some small, marble-like bumps. Surely not – this dodge was as old as the hills. I managed to squeeze up several pebbles from each of his five trout. He looked at me in feigned horror.

'I don't believe it, so help me God, the poor little dears must have been hungry, well, well, well!' He went around shaking his head, imploring the bystanders to commiserate with him. I just gave him a look, sending him on his way, but as he was leaving I called him back. He returned with a broad grin on his face.

'Paddy, my matches please.' After a fruitless search of his person he calmly replied, 'Would you know, they're gone, so they are.' Of course the man was incorrigible, but I was convinced sooner or later he would slip up. A pity really, for he was a likeable cove – nothing vicious about him at all, only this irresistible urge to cheat.

The fishing season was drawing to a close, and it had been a good one. October can be fickle, weather-wise; on this particular day a cold easterly was blowing, sending the fish into deep water. 'When the wind's in the east the fish bite least' proved to be correct, for of the twenty or so rods that had been fishing only three remained on the banks, and the time was only three-thirty in the afternoon. It looked as if it was going to be a cold night.

I decided to go home for a while, as I fully expected to be called out on a poaching incident. The autumn run of salmon was in full swing, and reports from the estuaries suggested that salmon and sea-trout were making their way up the river to the spawning grounds. Professional poachers know this, and consequently activity on the rivers increases. I received a telephone call at eight-thirty from a colleague who informed me that he would be round to my house within the hour. He did not enlarge on the blunt statement but he did hint, however, before replacing the receiver that it would be of interest to me.

My fellow bailiff arrived, looking decidedly pleased with himself as he settled down by the fireside nursing a large Scotch. I waited expectantly, David purposely keeping me on tenterhooks.

'Come on then, let's have it,' I urged.

'Well, you'll never believe it – we got the "parentless" blighter, what a bloody cheek he's got!' David paused, slowly filling his pipe.

'For Christ's sake man – who, what, why the suspense?'

David looked straight at me and said, 'Your Irish flanneller,' blowing a stream of pungent smoke in the air and watching it spiral to the ceiling.

I refused to be drawn, remaining silent as I too sipped my drink.

'As you know, you circulated the number to the boys. Well, on my way home I saw this vehicle parked in an unusual spot not far from the river. I found the registration number to be matey.' He paused for effect, passing me his now empty glass. 'Nice drop of malt that, Bob.' I refilled his tumbler. 'I left my car and walked overland down to the pool, and there was "nutty slack" sitting in a bush watching the floats of a net strung across the narrows. I nabbed him as he landed a freshly run salmon of about twelve pounds. It was a superb fish. I must say he was visibly shaken – so much so, do you know what he said?'

'What?'

'Would I give him a fag, his heart was fair breaking. I felt sorry for the poor old bugger and gave him one. On the way to the station I cautioned him and he said that he only had a few months to live and would I let him go? I asked him if he knew you and he said yes, and that you would confirm his illness. Anyway, he's due next month at Exeter.'

I informed David that to my knowledge the man was fit and well, had a record and was a liar. Why he should have asked me to confirm his impending death I do not know. Perhaps he had read my thoughts.

He was duly fined – that was two years ago. Now Paddy is back at Rainbow Bay – mind you, not so often as he used to be, but still asking for 'a little ole cigarette'. What can I do?

Of course – I give him one.

6

The Cronzgy Fly

Last night I attended the anglers' annual dinner, renewing many old acquaintances, some of whom I hadn't seen for years. The wine flowed freely, the meal was good, and for me, the best time of all was when I managed to waylay an angler who had a devastating sense of humour, as you will soon learn.

Alan was a hearty sixty-five-year-old who had spent most of his life abroad. He had farmed in Africa for a number of years, and his face bore the marks of that punishing life out in the searing heat. Though his once burly frame had run to fat, he gave the impression of being a rough handful, and the laughter lines deeply etched around his eyes, would, without warning, crease in loud, gutsy laughter. He drank like a fish, and was always ready with his superb wit; a much-liked fellow indeed.

We chose a quiet corner of the hotel and, over a brandy, talked of his last visit to the waters. After about fifteen minutes' reminiscing and more drinks, he suddenly remarked in his bluff, colonial accent, 'Hey, does old "Toffee Nose" still fish the lakes?' It took a little time for me to recall the particular man to whom he referred, so he prompted me with 'You know, the cove who was the world's greatest bore!' Still I was puzzled. 'Yeah, you know – the fella with the cronzgy fly. Jesus, that cove sure was a pain in the arse!'

I smiled as I remembered. 'Why yes, how could I ever forget,' I answered. 'No, I haven't seen him for the past five years or so. I heard he went back up north.'

'Let's hope he stays there,' my companion replied. 'I suppose some other poor sport is being bored to death. Jesus, when I think of the hours that twit followed me

46

around the waters – still, I guess he won't try that again in a hurry.' He finished the sentence with a loud laugh as he reached for his glass.

It happened several years ago. Alan had just arrived in England, coming to fish the lakes, and he soon became popular with his easy, friendly manner and was always ready to give advice, being a first-class fisherman. Many a prize fly he gave away to a not-so-successful angler. He was a good man.

About the same time another had joined the fishing fraternity, having recently moved into the county. Tall and angular, he wore a loud checked fishing suit complete with 'Sherlock Holmes' hat festooned with brightly coloured flies and lures. On his small, middle-aged feet he sported bright green, studded waders, although I did tell him that as wading was not permitted at the fishery a pair of ordinary sea-boots would suffice. Looking at me as at a bad smell, he retorted in an attempted, disguised Midlands accent, 'My dear boy, if I want to wade I shall; where I come from I was the squire you know!' I gently but firmly reminded him that the fishing rules would apply to him regardless; failure to comply would simply mean that he would not be able to fish here.

From time to time I would see him abusing the rules, and when admonished he would give one of his favourite smirks, mumbling under his breath, 'Little bloody Hitler!' However, although he was very trying, he soon settled down once he found that his pseudo-superior ways cut no ice with the other anglers.

It didn't take him long to cotton on to Alan; being the kind of chap Alan was, 'Toffee' tried to fish alongside him whenever it was possible. Needless to say, it soon became intolerable and Alan gave him a wide berth.

It was nearly the end of the season when it happened. At half-past four in the afternoon I was approaching the bay; Alan and Toffee were fishing within yards of each other. Reaching Alan first, I saw that he had captured four decent-sized rainbows.

'They look good.'

'Yeah, can't go wrong Bob. Bob, that bloke,' he said, nodding towards 'Toffee', 'gives me the bloody willies.

Every five minutes he comes and chats, asking me what fly I'm fishing with, can I spare him one as he can't catch fish. If I move he follows; it's no good, I shall have to tell him to blow – kids his bloody self.'

I left Alan and made my way to Toffee. 'Good afternoon – how's your luck?' I asked in a friendly though distant manner. He stopped fishing, replying, 'How is it that he's caught fish' – jerking his rod towards Alan – 'and I haven't had a touch although I am using the same fly as him?' I mumbled something about technique and left him.

Alan had stopped fishing, calling out to me to hang on as he was coming my way to the top of the lake. As he drew alongside, Toffee said, 'Alan, now look here, you're an artful old beggar – what's the secret, eh?'

A wicked look came into Alan's eyes, and he replied, 'Well, all right then, if I tell you my secret it will cost you a large Scotch.'

'Yes! Yes! Anything. I'm fed up with you always catching fish and I go home with an empty bag – what's the secret?'

'Out in Africa the natives are real good fishermen. They don't have any of your fancy tackle and flies, no, they just use a small feather, like one of your muddlers, but it's what they do with it that makes certain they catch fish.' Toffee's eyes widened, eagerly urging him to continue. Alan was enjoying every minute of it. 'Well chum,' he continued, lighting up a small cigar, 'you might not want to do it, but I always do.'

Toffee was getting impatient. 'Come on man, what is it?'

'Well, you get hold of your lure and rub it on your body – where you sweat most – and the scent drives them crazy. They call it the *cronzgy* fly.'

Alan watched his face closely and Toffee replied, 'I don't fancy that – oh no! Are you sure the fish come to it?'

'Please yourself mate – cheerio!'

We continued our walk, Alan remarking that that would keep the old buzzard quiet for a bit.

By now we were out of sight of our friend and had stopped to watch a huge brown trout cruising close to the bank; all was still and peaceful. Suddenly a painful, loaded shout echoed across the waters.

'Alan! Alan! Can you hear me? Alan quick!'

'Why, the old coon has caught a fish. Hang on Bob, I'll just go back and see.'

A good ten minutes later he appeared with a grin on his face.

'How big is it?' I enquired.

Drawing into the trees, he replied 'What do you think? The crafty old bugger went behind a bush and gave the fly the treatment. Serves him right; that'll keep him quiet for a while. It's not a fish he's caught!'

To remove the lure it was necessary for Alan brutally to use pliers to extract the offending object from his nether

region. This was executed – the word was most apt – by pushing the hook up through the loose skin of his testicles.

Most painful!

7

Percy Pays the Penalty

Percy Fairweather was at a disadvantage from the day of his entry into this cruel world. Why in heaven's name should he inherit the name of Fairweather? His life had been anything but.

He was a sad little man, with a face like a dried prune and a permanent drip on his nose summer and winter alike. One felt instinctively sorry for him. He could be found fishing the waters anywhere, anytime, with his line invariably tangled and his fly hooked in the nearest tree, shrub, trouser leg, hat – and even himself. I had to my recollection retrieved a Blue Dun, Black and Peacock Spider and, appropriately, a Bloody Butcher from his ear, nose and neck during one season alone.

He had fallen into the lake twice – he cannot swim – lost his net twice, dropped his cigarettes in the water more than once, and lost his keys, season permit, wallet, false teeth and countless flies. While all around caught fish, Percy never seemed to take even a tiddler. That is, until recently. But I am getting ahead of myself.

Percy Fairweather was by trade a butcher's assistant. He hated his job, his wife, the world, the government, in fact he even hated himself; but he loved fishing, he really did. He read every book on fly fishing, had the finest collection of flies and lures I have ever seen, and was the proud possessor of two Hardy split-cane rods, not forgetting the latest in carbon fibre and the best reels, fishing hat and waistcoat. But alas, he could not catch fish – even on opening day, when the waters would be stocked to the gunwales.

I would approach Percy with a word of encouragement, offering him a cigarette or the latest fly, and tell him that if he went further down the bank where I knew the fish were moving he would catch one. He would take the cigarette, and to the latter just give me a wry smile and say, 'Do you wanna bet?' Yes, I felt compassion for this sad, inoffensive little man.

After sunset one could find him drinking his glass of dark beer, always alone in the local public bar. Even his home-made shag cigarette looked sad as it drooped from his wizened little mouth. But still his passion for fishing was a burning desire that radiated from him like the sun.

Just once he was destined to bask in brief glory. That June day was simply superb, the right amount of ripple and cloud cover, and fish were everywhere, just like a stew pond. I started my patrol feeling on top of the world. On turning into the bay I came across a terrific uproar. There was Percy going berserk, jumping up and down, face contorted, his eyes bulging like organ stops. He was laughing, crying and cursing all at the same time. I thought he had thrown a fit. With him were three anglers all looking at a huge brown trout, a natural fish of about fifteen pounds laid out in state on the bank. It was a wonderful sight – in fact a British record!

Percy saw me and ran to me with arms outstretched. I thought he had finally cracked, and it was fully five minutes before I was able to understand him.

'I've caught a fish! Me who is no bloody good – I've caught a fish! It's mine I tell you, my very own! Damn the lot of you, I've caught a monster. It's a record, drinks all round! I'll show the old woman that I can catch fish.'

I managed to calm him down while we weighed the trout. Several fishermen gathered around to congratulate him, but he wasn't listening. He went on again, 'She thinks I'm a fool, I'll show her.'

'What did you catch it with?' ventured one angler.

'A Baby Doll, my last one – all the rest are up in the trees. Who cares – I've done it at last!'

We managed to get Percy on to his motorcycle with his precious trophy safely aboard, but as usual the bike wouldn't start; a stream of abuse echoed through the fishery. Eventually we gave him a push and he roared away in a cloud of blue smoke. Percy was not to be seen again, or indeed anywhere in the free world. Once again, his bad luck was to take over.

By the time Mr Percival Fairweather came to a halt outside his terraced house that was indistinguishable from the others, he was fairly calm. His wife, as usual, was at the bingo hall, so he laid his prize fish on the table and then, leaving the trout, rode the ten miles to his boss to ask if he could deposit the trout in the firm's deep freeze. He intended to have it mounted after the local press had photographed the record fish. A TV fishing programme had also been informed.

Meanwhile, Mrs Fairweather and her two friends arrived

home. Seeing the fish she exclaimed in her loud, coarse voice, 'Fancy bringing that ruddy thing home. I bet he bought that – stupid man.' And she began to hack the noble trout into three portions, giving her friends a piece each. 'The cat can have the head,' she said. The once proud fish was a sorry sight indeed.

Percy arrived home happy and excited: the press would be coming tomorrow, and permission had been granted to put his prize in the freezer. He went into the kitchen. One look at the despoiled fish remains was enough; Percy went completely mad, causing his wife fatal injuries.

Following his trial, Percy was sent to prison not far from here; a moorland stream containing little brownies flows nearby. His cell companion was an avid reader of fishing books, and not long after Percy's arrival his mate said, "Ere, what yer fink, the guv'nor has introduced a new study – fly fishing for beginners. What about having a go mate?'

Percy did – but not at fly fishing. He lost his remission before he even started his sentence!

8

Mathew

Since eleven that morning I had been waiting for a consignment of several hundred rainbow trout, but so far they hadn't arrived. In this day and age I find that bad time-keeping seems to be prevalent in all walks of life, which makes me sad. A spell of two years before the mast I am sure would cure the malaise. Anyway, that's the mood I was in as I sat on the bank 'champing at the bit'.

Several anglers had arrived at the lake, pausing on their way to the upper waters to enquire of me as to the state of the fishing, and also of my apparent bad temper, which was becoming more noticeable by the minute. I contented myself with rehearsing a reprimand that I intended to give to the fish transporter; I was already late with my routine chores and had at least a couple of hours to make up. A friendly farmer passed by on the narrow lane that ran alongside the water, waving a salutation. I waved back half-heartedly; I was behaving like a spoiled brat, working my irritation off on other kindly folk. Standing up, I kicked savagely at a fallen twig; mentally shaking myself, I decided I must behave more like an adult.

At precisely five-to-three Mathew arrived, heralding his arrival with a blast on the horn and a big, smiling wave. Without returning the greeting, I strode up the bank to the roadside to confront him.

'What time do you call this? Four bloody hours I've been waiting; I have a lot of work to do without wasting all this time!' I exploded. The steady hum of the oxygenator plant supplying life-giving air to the tanks of fish prevented him from hearing me. With a big grin on his boyish, friendly face he said gently, 'Pardon, Bob?' I was completely subdued by his soft, friendly manner, and my anger melted as I modified my question.

'What caused the delay – I expected you at eleven?'

'Sorry Bob, I got a puncture the other side of Tavistock. That was bad enough – then one of the oxygen bottles went on the blink. I don't suppose I'll be finished until eleven tonight. I've another delivery to make after yours. Still, never mind – are you keeping well? You'll be pleased Bob, I've got some special fish for you – some over three pounds.'

He continued preparing for the unloading, non-stop, without listening to whether or not I was replying to his conversation. That was typical Mathew.

Now I ask you, how in the name of God can anyone be angry with such a character? Mathew was in his mid-thirties, tall and slim with a shock of tousled reddish hair and a perpetual grin that stretched from ear to ear. During the years I've known him he has never been any different. He was one of the most conscientious men I have ever met and one of nature's nice guys – almost to a fault.

If it was pelting down with rain, or the sun was blazing hot, or even on the one occasion I have seen him fall flat in thick mud, he would always emerge smiling and apologetic. When the unloading had been completed he would gently spurn any help that he was offered to reload the wagon. 'No that's all right, thank you all the same, I prefer to do it myself – you know what I mean, don't you?' We never did, but invariably let him have his own way.

To watch Mathew manoeuvre his vehicle was classic: with trailer loaded with fish and with agonising slowness and perfection, he would position the load; my goodness – the time he would take. When time is of the essence it is sometimes necessary to cut corners and take chances; not so Mathew – nothing would, or could, ruffle him, and this sometimes led to noisy confrontations with his colleagues.

But there was to come a time when even his placid temperament failed to meet the occasion; however, this was later, and has been remembered in the context of the classic roles of the bailiff service of the south-west.

Mathew Jackson joined the river board at the age of eighteen; this tall, slim, clean-cut, friendly soul seemed ideal material for a trainee bailiff. He was well liked and very willing to undertake any task that was given him. Mind you, it became a bit much to see his ever-grinning face no matter how early or late in the day it was, or how adverse the conditions on the rivers. Nevertheless, he seemed to progress nicely – that is, until his first encounter with poachers.

It soon became evident, not only to water bailiffs but also to himself, that Mathew was unable to enforce the law with any recognisable authority – he was simply too damn nice. Of course, the word soon got around (it usually does) as to how easy he was, with the inevitable result – the poachers were having a field day. However, all due respect to Mathew: he requested that he be taken off the river as an enforcement officer and, if possible, 'Is there another job I could do please?'

As I have said, he was just one of those chaps one couldn't help liking, and eventually he was given the job of fish transporter, supplying fish from the hatchery to all the county's fisheries and rivers, a task in which he excelled. Without question he was, as one fisheries officer described him, a very professional man – praise indeed! He nursed and treated the fish with the same tenderness that a young mother lavishes on her first born.

Our story begins one warm morning in the month of June. A fish survey was needed on the top of the river, an area south of Foxtor mire, one of the largest bogs on Dartmoor. Mathew had been given a brand-new white Land-Rover. Have you ever seen the face of a child on Christmas morning opening his presents? Well, multiply that by a thousand and you will know what I mean – he was beside himself with joy. His dear wife, who was of exactly the same nature as himself, made little floral cushions for the cab, and two dinky little curtains for the back window. Inside he installed a little transistor radio and, at his own expense, bought rubber mats – very grand – for the deck. Each dial and control button was tabulated in black plastic tape spelling out their different functions. It was immaculate!

His love for it – for that is what it was – bordered on the ridiculous. Visitors were told, not requested, not to stand, lean or indeed touch the precious wagon. On one occasion he literally refused to take any leave for fear of someone else using the machine. What is more, for some unknown reason when he did take a week off at the boss's insistence, the Land Rover was not available for use!

Mathew had gone to great lengths to protect his vehicle with sacks of all shapes and sizes as he alone loaded the equipment needed for the fish survey – he was convinced the others were not careful enough. The team consisted of the head bailiff, one water bailiff and two technicians, plus one dog, Mathew acting as driver and general factotum.

Mud from HB's rubber boots smudged the inside of the cab; it was rubbed off immediately with a silent look of disapproval before the engine was started for the long climb to the moor. As usual the roads were busy with holidaymakers, although it was only just after nine in the morning, and progress was slow, especially along the narrow lanes on the moor, which necessitated much reversing. The painstaking way in which Mathew executed these manoeuvres irritated HB, who felt he was behaving, as he put it, like a big girl. Both bailiffs had lit cigarettes and were being watched by Mathew from the corners of his eyes, as they flicked the spent ash nonchalantly on the floor of the cab.

Soon the party arrived at the disused railway track, where a superb panoramic view of Plymouth unfolded; the sun was now becoming quite warm, and the sparkling waters of Plymouth Sound in the distance looked enchanting. A request from the back of the Land-Rover to stop was heeded as the three men wanted to 'pump ship', as did the dog, and it was some time before the terrier was enticed back on board, which really annoyed HB. For ten miles they travelled along the track until they reached the open-cast lead mine. One mile short of the mine the wagon left the track, descending to the head-waters of the river where the operation was to begin.

HB marked the passage with the customary yellow flags until they were all used, but there was still some way to go across the treacherous area. However, he walked out in front, telling the driver to follow through the long grass that carpeted the area. The weight of the vehicle squashed a distinct trail through the growth, disturbing several red grouse that rose in noisy alarm.

By the time the gear was unloaded and placed in position it was lunchtime. A small fire was lit for a fry-up; the taste of a bacon sandwich high up on the moor on a summer's day was quite something. The rugged grandeur and complete solitude in company with the wildlife is an experience that is never forgotten.

Hunger appeased, the men relaxed before starting work – but not Mathew, who was inspecting his precious machine, rubbing off imaginary spots on the shiny metallic surface. Glances of undisguised incredulity passed between the team as HB touched the arms of the resting men to witness this act of affection. It seemed to get under his skin; brushing off the fronds of dried grass from his trousers, he signalled work, and the team made their way to the river in the mellow sunshine.

In perfect conditions the survey was completed, with some fish being recorded. Mathew was permitted to reload the equipment alone at his request while the others completed their notebook entries. At last they were ready to leave, except for the little dog, who had wandered off in exploration of this doggy paradise. HB wasn't too happy to be held up, wishing to get away from this difficult spot. However, after a lot of calling and searching the terrier emerged, panting, its long tongue lolling from its mouth as though it had enjoyed the excursion in the scrub.

They started off on their homeward journey. After a short while, however, a look of apprehension crept over Mathew's face, and he peered through the windscreen with exaggerated concentration. He looked towards HB as though silently requesting confirmation. Sensing the tension, HB looked directly at him, asking, 'What's the matter?'

'I can't see the tracks – the grass has sprung back – is this the right way do you think?' Mathew asked in tremulous tones.

HB peered through his field-glasses for the yellow markers, but failed to sight the safe track. The Land-Rover crept slowly along, with the driver becoming visibly alarmed.

It all happened with frightening swiftness: the vehicle

began to sink steadily until only the spare wheel on the bonnet was visible. Mathew stared in utter disbelief, swallowing hard and turning to HB like a little boy lost. It was impossible to open the doors of the cab, so they scrambled out through the back window through which the rest of the crew had already left for firmer ground. The full realisation of the drama hit Mathew; like a man possessed, he began shovelling at the morass. Sweat poured from him as he burrowed non-stop, completely disregarding everyone else. After a while he managed to uncover the winch that sat above the front bumper, but alas – where to winch to? His body was now wringing wet with the Herculean effort; having done all that he knew how, he looked to the others for advice. The obvious and only answer was to leave the bogged vehicle and return to the nearest civilisation.

Mathew's face was a study; if he could, he was prepared to stay with his wagon all night. HB just gave him a withering look. Already it was becoming dark, and they had travelled only about three hundred yards from the sight. Now came the difference of opinion as to which direction to take after reaching the railway track. The darkness had descended very quickly.

HB and the two technicians, with Mathew of course, decided to turn right, but the bailiff – with his dog, which he loved – insisted that the direction should be left, despite the contrary view of the experienced moorman. He went off, unbeknownst to him heading towards the treacherous mire in the blackness. Hessary Tor aerial twinkled in the sky and the lights from distant Plymouth could now be seen, but the magnificent panoramic splendour was wasted on the party owing to the utter stupidity and obstinacy of one man.

A quick decision was taken, with HB going off in search of him, telling the main party to stand fast. Thankfully, the errant bailiff had by now changed his mind and was found heading towards the others. The night air echoed to the blast that was given, and even the dog showed surprise at the variety of the expletives.

They reached the village with everyone dead tired and hungry, and met a search party just ready to leave. At least they were safe, if red-faced with acute embarrassment.

Mathew

Before HB had started his breakfast next morning, Mathew was knocking on his door, with yards of towing cable wrapped around his body and grinning from ear to ear.

'Good morning Malc – all right then? 'Tis a nice morning, all dry like.' The enthusiastic greeting was received with some reserve.

'Where are the rest of the boys?' asked HB, peering out of the front door.

'We're meeting at Postbridge,' replied Mathew, his face now serious, eager to start on the rescue of his love.

'Come in and have a coffee before we go,' invited HB.

Mathew made a great effort to give the impression that he was enjoying the steaming hot drink, while watching every mouthful HB was taking, as though urging him on in his impatience to get going.

The drive over the moor was idyllic in the early sunshine. Several sheep lay on the roadside in isolated groups, necessitating careful navigation, and this seemed to increase Mathew's agitation whenever the car's pace slowed. They met the main party by the old clapper bridge amidst a flurry of good-natured taunts directed at Mathew: 'Your Land-Rover has probably sunk out of sight by now,' and 'It's more than likely poachers have stripped everything.'

His face had now taken on a morbid, unsmiling look as he sat in the back of the replacement vehicle, staring out towards the rocky landscape. During the journey he could be seen talking to himself and frequently biting his lip, a sure sign of nerves. This time they had ensured an adequate supply of flags were on board and the dog had been left at home. HB was determined that nothing was going to go wrong or distract him this time. Mathew did not speak one word to the others during the entire journey.

The first time he permitted himself a smile was when the Land-Rover was sighted, still there, wallowing in the bog like some bloated white hippopotamus in the sunshine. He was the first off, moving cautiously towards his beloved vehicle; he was actually seen to give the bodywork a caress as he gingerly fastened the cable, saying softly, 'Soon have you out, old girl.'

The safe area had been well and truly way-marked, and the mass of yellow flags fluttering in the strong breeze gave it the look of a medieval jousting tournament. A local had been engaged with his powerful tractor to assist recovery, and by half-past ten both vehicles were ready to begin. Last-minute checks were made until HB was satisfied and then the engines burst into life, the noise sending the surrounding wildlife scurrying off in panic. Cables became taut, wheels spun, sending spumes of peat and mud into the air; Mathew was even putting his shoulder to the stricken vehicle which, although doing no earthly good whatsoever, appeared to satisfy his impatient desire to rescue it. A further fifteen minutes of grumbling and cursing brought it onto firm ground amidst cheers.

Mathew grinned, producing two large flasks of coffee which he had brought for the occasion. Offering the men cups, he kept up a continual flow of 'Thanks, thank you – all right Malc? Not too much damage is there? All right Tom? Thanks – all right Charlie? Thank you,' and so on.

Although it looked scruffy covered in foul-smelling sludge, the Land-Rover was mechanically sound. With a fanatical burst of energy, Mathew attempted to clean off the mess, much to the amusement of the others. The rescue accomplished, everyone returned to base – another lesson learned the hard way.

By the way, if in your travels around the authority's reservoirs or rivers you happen to see a sparkling, gleaming white Land-Rover delivering fish you would be well advised not to lean, touch, or even look too closely at it – ever since the bogging incident Mathew has been a bit odd. He has painted on the side of the bonnet *My Angie*, and his wife now swears she takes second place in his affections.

Last week a certain bailiff became enraged with Mathew's unpunctuality and actually kicked the front wheel. At present Mathew Jackson faces a disciplinary charge.

9

One Man and His Dog

I first met him fishing a remote reservoir in the heart of Dartmoor. In fact, it would be more correct to say that I had stumbled on him.

Spring had arrived late on Dartmoor after a severe winter, and the mid-morning sun was beginning to warm as I walked the two miles to the dam. In order for me to view the lake I had to climb a steep gorse-covered bank, and frankly, my legs were already aching after the long riverside walk, which was strewn with massive granite boulders.

My recent appointment as bailiff-warden of the Dartmoor lakes had taken me to several large areas of still waters; this was the last one to visit. It was completely unknown to me. A wide expanse of still, peaty water seemed to sit on a high plateau covering many acres before eventually spilling over in a spectacular display into the winding river, some sixty feet or so below. The dam was constructed of gigantic granite blocks that reminded one of an ancient fortress, and during the winter millions of gallons of turbulent, white-capped water tumbled over, often with an umbrella of noisy seagulls hovering over the fall. It made a dramatic spectacle.

On reaching the summit I surveyed the reservoir with the aid of my field-glasses; all seemed deserted, except for a brief moment when I thought I detected a movement. A short elbow of land reached out into the water forming a kind of cove, and by the water's edge I saw what appeared to be a wandering dog. I decided to explore the area and began to walk the uneven, narrow track around the perimeter.

At the extreme end of the lake I could see a whitish blur contrasting with the drab colour of the moorland. Through my glasses I made out a small feeder-stream bubbling in, with the gaunt outline of a solitary heron fishing. I looked in vain for the dog; it had completely vanished.

The going was now becoming much harder, for a mass of rocks covered the hillside leading to the water's edge. I decided to rest for a while, choosing a nearby boulder. The sun was warm and, removing my hat, I basked in the superb atmosphere of the tranquil surroundings. The plaintive cry of a distant curlew echoed across the water; closing my eyes, I breathed deeply of the virgin air perfumed with heather and gorse.

The frantic alarm call of a disturbed pheasant finally broke my reverie, and I rose somewhat reluctantly to continue my walk. All around me was a scene of utter isolation and wild beauty. A recent hatch of heather-fly had tempted the trout to feed and the entire lake was peppered with widening rings as I reached the end of the waters, crossing the rough railway-sleeper bridge that spanned the narrow feeder-stream.

A kingfisher flew upstream in a sudden burst of colour, pricking the surface of the water with its wake. I was now on the true left bank (the flow behind me) making my way back to the dam, a distance of about a mile. After about a quarter of a mile, without warning a small dog appeared from a fold in the hillside, growling menacingly, and stopping me in my tracks. A fat pug eyed me with large, bulbous eyes, wheezing with throaty grumblings.

I looked around for its master, searching further along the bank, which was practically hidden by the tall, wiry grass. The dog came hesitantly towards my legs and I used my stick to discourage it, when a similar gutsy growl came from a hollow in the bank a few yards away. Was it human? What species, I wondered, was capable of producing that kind of noise?

A small, round, unshaven face emerged from the reeds, looking not so much enquiringly but with a downright 'What the bloody hell do you want disturbing me' attitude. He made no attempt to silence the pug, who was by now wheezing and growling while attempting to seize my ankles.

At last the man showed himself fully on the pathway. He was in his late sixties, rotund, and was wearing a squashed tweed hat smothered in coloured flies, some of which still bore traces of nylon thread hanging in disordered array. The scruffy, well-worn jacket, with streaks of snuff stains on the lapels, strained at his large gut by a single leather button. As I moved closer to the water's edge, I noticed two bottles of beer tied with string hanging to cool in the water from a stick thrust into the bank.

Wishing him a good morning, I was met with a silent, arrogant stare. Announcing my identity, I asked him if he would silence this ball of fat. He merely slapped his short, fat leg and the dog reluctantly settled a few feet away in the

heather, daring me to make the slightest false move. The man himself looked like an escapee from a Dickensian novel: a diminutive Bill Sikes complete with a pseudo bull-terrier. I asked to inspect his licence, and for the first time he spoke.

How his accent belied his appearance! In a cultured voice, he insisted on first seeing my warrant of authority. Apologising, I produced the warrant, of which he made rather a laboured and, in my opinion, unnecessarily long study, hoping no doubt to find a possible flaw in the official notice.

After a lengthy pause, he made great play of the search for his licence. I couldn't help thinking he knew exactly where it was. At last, reaching into the back pocket of his trousers he produced a crumpled, tired-looking piece of paper which he thrust towards me growling, 'Is this what you want?' Signing the licence, I thanked him, leaving him muttering silent obscenities. Phew! The man was obviously an eccentric; I didn't like him at all.

On reaching the dam I descended to the roadway and the river, where two dipper birds were curtseying in the shallows, the sun reflecting on the gold-coloured pebbles. The unpleasant little man was temporarily forgotten.

It was to be several weeks and patrols before I met him again, but this time at a different lake. Many boats were out on this superb July day, with just the right amount of cloud and ripple for a good day's fishing. Many holiday visitors were in the country and, so far, it had been a good season all round. The reservoir I was to check was sandwiched between vast conifer plantations, and ancient hut circles squatted on the water's edge – an excellent venue in which to relax and fish, either in a boat or from the bank. The lake was fed by a series of small feeder-streams that came in off the moor, the haunt of heron and duck.

Not far from the feeder-streams was a small boggy area, and although it was a good productive spot for indigenous brown trout that weighed from a quarter to half a pound, it was considered hazardous and few anglers fished there. I made my patrol by boat, checking and having the odd conversation with the anglers until I reached a lone woman fishing near the dam, well away from the other fishermen.

Beaching my craft, I walked the fifty-odd yards along the bank to reach her, and offered a good morning to this square, matronly lady who began slowly to retrieve her line. Strands of grey hair escaped from the close-fitting woollen hat, giving her an almost girlish look, while a token smear of lipstick had been given to her thin lips, resulting in a scarlet slash. However, although she was dressed in masculine, drab-coloured oilskin jacket and trousers, some attempt had been made to signify that she was in fact of the feminine gender. Her eyes, ringed with mascara, surveyed me with cool disdain.

When I asked to inspect her licence, she literally spat, 'Is this necessary? Really, so tiresome!'

Laying down her rod she began to search her haversack, which by the look of it contained everything bar the kitchen sink. After disposing of a packet of cream crackers, tomatoes, cheese, thermos, flies and more, she finally produced the required document. The bending had brought a flush to her face, revealing a cord-like vein on her forehead. She looked annoyed and extremely hot and bothered.

Her oilskin trousers had become loose and had slipped a little from her waist; she hitched them up with an irritable action. In the heat of the sun this temporary exertion had caused her to perspire, sending rivulets of black from her eyes. I thanked her, wishing her good fishing, only to receive a snort in reply as I continued on in the boat.

During the midday break more anglers had arrived, swelling the banks to at least twenty or so fishermen. I thought of the bad-tempered lady that I had met earlier and conceived a wicked thought: she would make an ideal companion for 'Bill Sikes'. The more I thought of it the more determined I became of arranging an 'accidental' meeting between the two unfriendly people at the earliest opportunity. After all, I mused, they deserved each other.

The afternoon saw many boats on the water, some of the occupants lying back enjoying the sunshine, their fishing rods temporarily in-board. I passed them at low speed as I made my way to the extreme end of the lake, a favourite spot of mine for enjoying the solitude of wildlife, and for checking the volume of water coming in from the moor. Several anglers waved in recognition as I neared the end of the reservoir. Finally, pushing the boat ashore among a cluster of wandering willows, the exposed roots reminding me of a mangrove swamp, I splashed ashore.

So engrossed was I in checking my notebook that I failed to see an approaching angler; it was the growling, or should I say the asthmatic wheezing, of a dog that caused me to look up. It was, of course, the pug, who heralded its master plodding a little way behind.

'Any fish moving?' was the curt demand.

'I haven't noticed any yet. I've only been here a short while.'

'I see.'

With that scintillating piece of conversation he continued on his way, followed by his little fat companion. He finally stopped a little way past the feeder-stream; here he was completely alone. I watched him begin to prepare his tackle, while the pug proceeded to lift a leg on every available log and rock, as much as to say, 'This is my territory – keep away!' I had no desire to remain anywhere near these unfriendly creatures, so I headed back upstream in the boat, eventually stopping a little distance away from the oilskin-clad lady. As I approached she offered not the slightest recognition, looking straight ahead over the water.

'Have you caught any yet?' I enquired, in an enforced friendly manner.

'No!' she snapped, casting her line out with venom. I was determined to break down this indifference to – or was it dislike of? – the male species.

'I have seen several fish moving down at the other end of the lake; it would seem they are taking small black gnats,' I volunteered cunningly. A faint flicker of interest showed on her face.

'Really? Where exactly?'

It wasn't until I offered to take her down in the boat that she really thawed.

'I say, that's damn civil of you – right you are.'

She collected her gear and climbed aboard.

However, we travelled downstream in complete silence. I put her ashore some twenty yards away from 'Sikes', who was hidden from view by rocks. She gathered her tackle around her, and unsmilingly uttered one word: 'Thanks.'

I resisted the urge to stay around to witness the eventual meeting of the two oddballs and headed back, though not before I heard the first barking of the dog. Perhaps I was doing both of them a favour by bringing these unhappy creatures together.

Several days later an overnight rain had refreshed the dusty countryside, giving it a sparkling brilliance, and the morning sun shone through the spindly willows, their branches festooned with jewelled droplets. It had been welcome, no matter how little; the long, dry days had reduced the feeder-streams to mere trickles, causing the young trout to retreat further upstream. However, the abundant hatch of fly had produced plenty of activity for the anglers. Catches had been good, especially during the evening rise.

My afternoon patrol had brought me to a little 'frying pan' bay that was visited all day long by dragonfly and blue damsels, chasing each other tirelessly over the still waters. A lone fisherman sat gazing out over the water, the smoke from his pipe curling in little eddies above his head before finally disappearing over the water. He was a regular visitor to the reservoir, one whom I had met and liked – a really knowledgeable angler. We discussed the world in general and the cup of coffee he offered me was welcome indeed.

'By the way, you missed quite a to-do the other day,' my companion began, easing his body into a more comfortable position. 'There I was, lying back watching a magnificent butterfly on the bush, when the continuous barking of a dog began to irritate me. Propping myself up, I saw this old dear changing her fly while this horrible pug snarled at her feet.

'She was becoming quite agitated, trying to shoo it away without much success. Standing up, further down the bank I could see a man fishing, but as he made no attempt to silence the beast I assumed the dog must have been a stray. I might tell you that I was also getting fed up with the constant yapping. I was about to go down to the dog when this old dear called out to the man, "I say, is this your dog?" The old boy went on casting his line, not even bothering to look in the direction of the voice. Once again she called out, at the same time trying to approach him, but was prevented by the ferocious pug. After two more casts she apparently decided enough was enough.

'Using the rod as a make-do lance, she advanced towards the old boy, disregarding the dog who, surprisingly enough, backed off, bewildered at the boldness of her move. As she reached the angler, the dog gained courage and snapped at her heels. She immediately thrust the rod at the dog's body, scoring a direct hit; the frightened, injured yell prompted the old man into action. The irate woman repeated her question once more as to the ownership of the brute.

' "Yes madam – why do you ask?"

' "Then will you keep the damn thing quiet – surely you are aware of the awful din it has been creating?"

'With exaggerated courtesy he said, "Madam – if you don't like it I suggest you fish elsewhere – the waters are big enough." After that profound statement he continued to fish with marked aplomb.

'The old lady went scarlet, telling him that she intended to stay put, and that his behaviour would be reported to the bailiff. After that drama she went back to her fishing. The dog calmed down, and sat near its owner chewing a biscuit that the old fella had thrown.

'It couldn't have been more than a couple of minutes when the barking began again. The old girl was ready this time and she began hitting the dog with her landing net, causing the cowardly animal to yelp, not so much in pain but in real terror, as the blows began to find their target. This proved to be too much for "Sikes", who came hurrying towards her yelling, "What the bloody hell, woman! Stop it at once – do you hear?"

'He attempted to wrestle the net from her, and this move was met with a series of savage blows. There was no question about it, she was by now demented. While all this was going on the animal kept up a continuous barking and snapping at her trouser leg. I felt that I must interfere, and quickly reaching the two I aimed a token kick at the pug. My sudden appearance out of the blue halted the affray and, strangely enough, silenced the dog. Startled, they both looked somewhat sheepishly at me, as they began to straighten their clothing to hide their apparent embarrassment. At least the old man did mumble an apology as he sidled off with his dog.'

Although I did meet the two of them a week later at different waters, neither made a complaint. I, of course, made no reference to the incident.

The fishing season was now drawing to a close; many anglers were either in Scotland or Ireland fishing the various

72

competitions or attending the salmon pilgrimage. Attendances on the lakes were sparse, apart, that is, from the hardy
regulars. I had really forgotten about the old man and his dog;
the season had been busy and I had met anglers from all over
the world.

Looking out of the permit office I could see about half-
a-dozen rods fishing; they were well spaced out along the
two-mile perimeter of the lake. A light breeze teased the
water sufficiently to produce a favourable ripple, while big
fluffy clouds afforded perfect cover for the anglers' lines and
a recent hatch of alder flies made for a good day's fishing.
I decided to do a patrol on foot rather than by boat: it was
one of those perfect days and I was determined to enjoy it
to the full.

A word here and there soon took care of most of the
morning and I, like the fishermen, was enjoying this bonus
of a perfect September day. Reaching the boggy area of the
lake, I was forced to make a longish detour through a small
area of scrubland, where I was able to cross a little stream
that entered the reservoir. Crossing the ancient stone bridge
that was used by pack-horses before the area was flooded, I
came face to face with 'Sikes' – minus his dog.

He was leaning heavily against one of the stone supports
of the bridge, looking deathly pale; he seemed to be having
difficulty in breathing. His abandoned fishing rod lay half in
the water, wedged in between two boulders. A small brown
trout swam aimlessly in circles on the end of the line in its
attempt to shake off the offending hook. I asked him the
whereabouts of his dog, but he was incapable of speech; he
just looked at me in bewilderment. His face had a queer,
lop-sided look which led me to believe he had suffered some
kind of stroke. Making him as comfortable as possible, I ran
as fast as I could back to the office to telephone for help.
Half-way back I met the arrogant woman and quickly told her
of my mission. Her manner changed dramatically; she at once
told me she was a retired hospital matron from a well-known
London teaching hospital and would attend immediately.

Eventually the ambulance arrived and I transported the
attendants by boat to the scene, where the patient was being
comforted by the ex-matron.

It wasn't before August the following year that I again met them both fishing together in a boat. They seemed to be perfectly relaxed together: I would dearly have liked to ask what had happened to the dog, but they were not those kind of people. However, I did offer my congratulations on the gentleman's recovery from his illness. 'It was nothing – nothing at all. Good day!' came the reply.

I pulled away from them in the boat, wondering what makes folk like that tick.

10

Head Bailiff

No sooner had the Land-Rover stopped than a wandering band of moorland ponies came cantering across the rock-strewn moor in search of any titbits that might be on offer. We stopped alongside a stream high on Dartmoor to carry out a survey of the fish population that is deemed necessary for the river authority records. The crew consisted of four water bailiffs and a lady biologist, who really went overboard for the unkempt, semi-wild ponies.

'Ooh – aren't they simply sweet?' she crooned, offering a couple of custard creams to a wet-nosed bay. The biscuits were taken with a sudden, rough thrust of its muzzle, briefly startling our Ada.

'I say, that's a bit naughty. Come now, be gentle,' she admonished, reaching in her haversack for more goodies.

Over the hill, behind a rising tor, the plaintive call of a curlew lingered in the morning air.

'Right lads, let's make a start. Careful with that net Dave, they're bloody expensive!' The head bailiff began to organise the operation. He was feeling fragile; there's nothing worse than a hangover when you've a wet, fiddly job to do. By now the rest of them had got the message, giving each other knowing looks in silent appraisal of his ill-humour. The nets were strung across the water, a hundred yards apart.

Dave, who was by far the biggest and undoubtedly the strongest, carried the portable generator in his two massive arms, as one would carry a sleeping child, positioning it on the bank. Although it weighed well over a couple of hundredweight, he barely took an extra breath, just giving a broad grin and requesting the next task; a most likeable and handy man to have behind you, especially at night on anti-poaching patrols.

The setting up of the equipment took the best part of an hour, and the effort had brought visible distress to the ailing HB.

'All right lads – coffee time,' he said, flopping down on the cropped grass and lying at full stretch. During the break Ada, drinking her coffee, idly probed a newly raised molehill with a ruler. The rest of the crew smoked, while HB lay very still with eyes closed.

By nine-thirty the sun had broken through, putting everyone in a happy mood, and even HB began to smile as he took charge of one of the probes, giving the order to start the generator. The sudden explosion of sound sent the nearby ponies off at a gallop, while two bailiffs began a systematic sweep of the measured area with the electrodes, probing the nooks and crannies of the moorland stream.

Soon tiny salmon and sea-trout parr were being drawn to the probe, slightly stunned by the charge of electricity, and were scooped up in the hand-net by the man following behind. The captured fish were deposited in big square keep-nets that were stationed at each end of the netted area in readiness for the biologist, who measured and tabulated the specimens. Apart from many fingerlings and parr, large eels and small brown trout were also attracted to the probes. This procedure continued until the length of the stretch had been traversed three times, thus giving a comprehensive picture of the density of fish.

Unfortunately, the slight improvement in HB's hangover had now taken a turn for the worse. River beds are notorious for their uneven and treacherous nature, and it was his unfortunate lot suddenly to disappear up to his neck in a deep hole that had obviously been excavated when the stream had been running low. Loud, watery oaths polluted the virgin moorland air as he broke the surface, and inadvertently grabbed the business end of the dropped electrode. Ada, who by the very nature of her profession was a broad-minded lass, blushed as she quickly stopped the generator and called sweetly with genuine concern, 'Are you all right?' She received no acknowledgement from HB, who was standing dripping on the bank. Water poured from every orifice, and his spectacles had somehow reached the back of his neck, which took on the colour of his florid face.

'Look at my bloody cigarettes, my watch!' he wailed. 'I knew it, I knew it!' he repeated, 'I somehow felt it wasn't going to be my day!' He began stripping off everything except his trousers, which had been partially saved in the ducking by his long waders and oilskin over-trousers.

From a nearby hawthorn two magpies eyed the half-naked apparition, and seemed to laugh in their croaking cackle as

they flew off, probably saying to each other, 'There's none so queer . . .'

Luckily, HB lived only a short distance away; with the help of a borrowed sweater, he drove home for a change of fresh clothing. By the time he returned the survey was almost completed, the netted fish having been returned unharmed to the water. Ada expressed her satisfaction with it, commenting on the excellent fertility of the stream.

Lunchtime was spent at the site in bright, warm sunshine and friendly banter. HB seemed to have benefited in more ways than one by his visit to his home: he fairly oozed good will and his complexion had deepened, aided somewhat by his Rabelaisian humour.

The lunchtime break was ended with HB jumping to his feet, at the same time issuing a loud burp. 'Right lads, one more job to do then we're finished. Dave, you and Robbie bring in the nets, the sooner we get cracking the better!' Within thirty minutes the Land-Rover was loaded and on its way to the valley, where the river levels and slackens pace after the hurried descent from the moor.

The progress of the Land-Rover was hampered by the density of holidaymakers' traffic along the narrow lanes, which meant much reversing and cursing, not only at the frequency of the manoeuvres but at the sheer inability of some drivers who, it seemed, were unable to reverse their own vehicle at all. It was HB who was the most affected, showing his displeasure by frequent reference to 'these bloody grockles!' Apparently he was anxious to get to the next site quickly and finish the survey, as he had an important meeting of the 'Buffs' to attend in the evening. Ada sat in front during the journey, silently studying the passing landscape and sucking a jumbo-sized mint; the rest sat in the back in company with the fishy-smelling equipment.

A party of holidaymakers leaned over the ancient granite bridge watching the flow of the river; one was busily photographing the water while a mother knelt by her school-boy son, dabbing at his grazed knee with a handkerchief which she moistened with her mouth. All eyes turned to watch the arrival of the party as it stopped on the verge by the bridge. As unloading began the visitors eased forward to the Land-Rover, obviously delighted with this unexpected bonus of interest.

It wasn't long before one floral-shirted male of about fifty with 'fair round belly with good caponed lined' demanded in a most arrogant, affected accent, 'And what would you be going to do?' HB, already eager to get on with the task with the minimum of delay, replied in a matter-of-fact way, 'Write a letter.' The intended sarcasm fell on stony ground, for a large-bottomed female in ridiculous shorts asked in a shrill, authoritative voice, 'What – didn't understand? Are you people some kind of fishermen?'

By now most of the gear had been stowed on the grass, with the onlookers pressing closer to examine it. 'Right – down the bank with it lads!' The order was given with complete disregard for the questioner. Ada did, however, explain briefly as to the nature of the exercise; she was immediately bombarded with many questions until after a while she, too, became weary of what she later described as 'an interrogation' and tersely took her leave.

The area of the survey was one of exquisite beauty and serenity; here the river flows reasonably level course, meandering through a deep-sided valley, heavily wooded for about six miles. Along the stretch are four bridges, all of granite, three gentle weirs and an abundance of wildlife. On this August afternoon the air was filled with the cooing of pigeons, the song of blackbirds and the sounds of the ever-moving water as it lapped the moss-covered boulders.

By now the nets were in position, and the generator throbbed into life at the start of the operation. The holidaymakers had drifted off, unable to watch, as the thick cover of riverside vegetation obscured the view. By the second sweep the keep-nets were already showing a healthy catch with a majority of salmon parr, which was encouraging. While the final phase of the survey was taking place, the head bailiff decided to have a smoke, satisfied with the time taken and the ease with which it was being completed. He chose an old, moss-covered log on which to sit and roll a cigarette from his new tin of tobacco. Lighting up, he slid down on the grass, using the log as a pillow. The rest of the lads were busy assisting Ada with her recording at a gentle, unhurried pace appropriate to the surroundings. A sudden, loud and agonised cry shattered the calm of the valley. All eyes focused in the direction of HB, who was running toward the deep pool followed by a blackish cloud of angry hornets. For a brief moment the bailiffs were dumbstruck with amazement; the splash as he dived head-first into the water brought them back to life, and they ran forward to help their colleague. But there was no way HB was coming out of the river and between gulps of air, he submerged himself completely until the marauding insects had gone.

Once again he stood dripping on the bank; this time, everyone was bursting with laughter, including Ada, who was verging on hysteria. HB made no attempt to dry himself; instead he calmly asked for a cigarette, shaking his head quietly and saying, 'I just do not believe it – twice in a day. I don't bloody care any more – no I don't, I just bloody don't!'

The team rallied, and between them rigged him out with an oilskin suit until he could be driven home, where his wife became convinced that there must be a conspiracy against her darling.

All that happened many years ago on the thirteenth day of August. That week, the Director of Fisheries received in his weekly report from his head bailiff not only the good news of the density of fish, but also a personal statement on the water quality of the Dartmoor rivers and the fecundity of insect life.

11

The Lovers

During the year patrolling the lakes and rivers of the south-west, one meets some interesting people. Each has a story to tell, sometimes one of great happiness; often, alas, one of sorrow. Of course, as a water bailiff I also get involved with lawbreakers; thankfully, these on the whole have been a minority. My story is about an ordinary, charming individual who enjoyed her fishing and the superb countryside of Devonshire.

I would see her often, fishing either the reservoir or the river, and on every occasion she radiated happiness and charm. It was always a pleasant quarter of an hour or so spent in her company; we would discuss the merits of the latest fly, or current sightings of fish on the beat. A cultured, intelligent woman, she was a comparative newcomer to the county, having arrived in Devon during the past year. Most of her early life had been spent in India, the daughter of a retired army officer, where, as she put it, she had been cosseted and sheltered from the harsher aspects of life. The death of both her parents, who had decided to remain in India after independence had forced her to return to England, where she had lived for a time with a distant relative.

Her education had been undertaken at a well-known English public school, where she had spent a happy but lonely time. After working in London as a fashion editor, she had decided to spend the rest of her days in Devonshire. Now in her early middle age, single and without kith or kin, she intended to 'stagnate' as she put it in this paradise of fishing. She could, I suppose, be described as a handsome woman; life had been kind to her, and the fair hair showed only the slightest suspicion of invading grey.

The county had been enjoying glorious summer weather, more so for the fishing: not too bright, with cloud, and the rivers had remained at a constant level. It had been one of those ideal summers when it rained mainly during the night, bringing sparkling, sunlit mornings. Absolutely perfect. I had noticed during the past month that Miss Elizabeth Palmer – that is the name I shall give her – was now in the company of a pleasant, middle-aged man who showed considerable skill with his fishing. On this particular morning he was teaching her to roll-cast a difficult part of the river.

The river flowed gently at this spot after its frantic journey off the moor; each side of the narrow flow was flanked by hardwood trees and unruly brambles, while honeysuckle entwined the gnarled branches – a perfect backcloth for the brightly coloured woodpecker who watched the flashing line as it landed the fly on the surging flow. The overnight rain had left the air washed and heavy with a pungent aroma of Douglas Pine, whose branches housed a family of squirrels.

I had been spotted, and the anglers waved recognition as I picked my way over the unruly boulders. A recent hatch of midge massed in tiny clouds over the water as it slurped over the weir, where several trout were rising. The anglers looked happy, making an ideal couple as they laughingly teased each other at their attempts at the difficult roll-cast. I accepted the invitation to share a coffee with them, sitting down on the bank surrounded by clumps of colourful celandine. The man lay back, pushing his hat over his eyes, and sighed contently.

'This really is heavenly.'

'I'm glad we've met this morning,' Miss Palmer began, 'I want you to be the first person to know,' looking down at the recumbent figure as though for confirmation.

He removed the hat and sat up, smiling at her as he took her hand. 'Peter and I are engaged,' and she shyly offered her ringed finger towards me. I congratulated them, wishing them every happiness in the world; it was indeed a very happy occasion on this lovely morning in such idyllic surroundings.

I met them many times towards the end of the fishing season, and on every occasion they seemed to be deeply in love. Sometimes I purposely avoided them, having no desire to intrude on the happy pair.

Winter had now arrived, with salmon coming up river from the Atlantic to the lonely spawning grounds high up on the moor. It was always an exciting time for me; in company with a colleague we would walk the rivers, plotting the 'redds' and of course keeping a weather eye on poachers at this vulnerable period. The first touch of frost triggers off the salmon's urge to spawn and, after selecting a suitable site on the pebbles, she excavates a depression in which to lay her eggs – a scene that has been enacted virtually since time itself began.

The river had now been reduced to a medium flow, and reeds and bankside herbage were in the grip of hard frost. Fallen trees covered in rime bore the robin's imprints, while a knee-high mist rolled off the bitterly cold water as we made our way upstream. Our footsteps crunched through the long, flattened grass covered in crusty frost; we had yet to find our first redd. A quarter of a mile past the stone bridge we reached the weir, the scene of last summer's happiness. I stopped to watch the surging water flowing softly over the weir, thinking of the happy anglers. A dipper bird joined us, squatting in the shallows, completely impervious to the intense cold, while our muted conversation was monitored by puffs of vapour.

All around us, apart from the sound of running water, was a blanket of silence. Wedged between rocks in a tiny backwater, a diseased salmon lay on its side, staring with eyeless sockets at the painted sky as the flow gently buffeted its fungus-covered flanks. We pressed on further towards the upper reaches where we would witness once again the annual ritual of the king of fishes.

The winter had passed without any spectacular happenings; apart from snow in late February it could have been termed a reasonably mild winter. Fishing had begun that month on the river, with many kelts (spawned fish) returning down river to the sea, exhausted and ravenous after spawning. Fishermen were complaining about the scarcity of fish – but then they have done since the last century. Nothing new!

April the first brought fishermen to the lakes in droves for the opening of the trout season, the waters having been heavily stocked. Friendships were renewed all along the bank after the winter lay-off. Once again, I met the happy pair fishing the lake, both looking radiant and devoted. I was told that the wedding was to take place in June, and duly received an invitation to attend. I was delighted to accept.

The season progressed well, with sometimes a big fish being landed, a few minor law-benders, and of course the ever-present salmon poachers. But I was puzzled – I hadn't seen anything of the two love-birds. I had covered the rivers and lakes, but had not seen anything of them at all. June arrived: still no word about the proposed marriage venue, and they had not been fishing, at least not in my area.

July was now well under way, and I had given up hope of seeing them. After all, I reasoned, there was no real reason why they should get in touch with me, a mere acquaintance. Still, I was a little disappointed, and felt I at least deserved an explanation.

It was the first week in September and I was on a routine patrol of the river, making my way up the valley towards the moor. The sun was shining and the leaves on the sycamore just beginning to turn; it certainly was a delightful morning. In the distance, just past the bridge, I could see a figure standing by the weir, the first angler I had spotted during the morning; at least it would add interest to have a ten-minute yarn. Approaching the figure, to my delight I saw it was Miss Palmer – or would it be Mrs somebody-or-other?

She stood by the oak, resting her hand against the rough trunk and gazing down into the swirling mass, looking pensive and subdued. Cheerfully I bade her good day, and she turned to face me – her face ravaged with suffering. She did not speak a word and I knew something dreadful must have happened.

'Are you all right?' I asked lamely, not really knowing quite what to say but feeling I must say something. She must have cried herself dry, for she looked at me with a vacant expression and after a moment's pause said in a slurred voice, 'He's not here now, you know.' Her breath reeked of whisky.

The Lovers

Gently taking her arm, I sat her on a nearby rock. She held her head in her hands, staring down at the moss where a single white daisy grew up through the thick carpet. The atmosphere was charged with immense sadness. A family of blue tits squabbled in the brambles, while coming downstream a pair of mallards hugged the bank, nosing the weed. I searched for a titbit to give them; at least it would give me something to do while I waited self-consciously for an explanation. She watched the ducks accept the bread and then, looking at me in a most direct way, said, 'I'm sorry – will you have a drink?' She reached for a part-bottle of whisky from her fishing bag.

She took a long pull from the bottle, which sent her coughing and spluttering as the raw spirit caught her breath. Shaking herself, she replaced the cap and returned the bottle to the bag, her invitation apparently forgotten. Lighting a cigarette with shaking fingers, she told me of her terrible sadness, faltering between each sentence as she fought desperately to control her sorrow. The frequent swigs she took caused me concern for her safety, especially in her present state of mind, but I could hardly prevent her, so I simply listened to her story.

A good half-hour passed; the ducks and blue tits had gone, and I had heard the complete account of her sorrow. Her fiancé had tragically been killed in a car crash just one week before the wedding, and since then her life had been hazy. She kept repeating, 'Why, oh why, what have I done to deserve this cruelty?' I felt totally inadequate, and wished I knew how to act in this situation; it was as if nature itself were paying silent homage to the unhappy tale.

After an agonising few minutes I asked gently if she would like me to walk her to the cottage that she had rented in the tiny village. She nodded her head like a tearful, lost child, so I began to collect her tackle together as she started to walk towards the narrow lane that ran parallel to the river. A few feet away from where I was standing, in a cleft of the oak, I picked up a small canvas package. As she was now ahead of me I couldn't confirm if it belonged to her, but assumed it must have come from her bag. I put it among the rest of her gear.

The walk back took us just over half an hour, during which time she seemed to recover her bearing. Although I made efforts to capture her interest in the wildlife I barely received an acknowledgement, apart from the casual nod and murmur. Reaching the tiny thatched cottage she turned and, in a voice barely audible, thanked me. I watched the door close behind her, feeling a trifle uneasy. Should I interfere and alert, say, a doctor – or what? Perhaps I was showing unnecessary concern. I reasoned that she had recovered somewhat during our walk and consoled myself that she would be all right.

The pressure of duties during the following weeks soon dispelled from my mind the imaginary ills that may have befallen Miss Palmer, and I settled down to routine tasks.

It wasn't until the following May that I was to meet her again, not by the river, but fishing the lakes. By the look of her she seemed to have recovered from her grief; greeting me warmly, she invited me to sit with her while she talked. How different was the story since we last met, and I must say what a wonderful end to her sorrow. Was it divine intervention?

Last year when I had taken her home, she had thrown herself onto the bed and cried uncontrollably for an hour, eventually falling into a deep sleep. She awoke cold, the moon shining through the window; the village clock struck ten. After taking a bath, she satisfied her hunger with just a milky drink and slept soundly until nine o'clock the next morning.

'I hope I'm not boring you – am I?' I hastened to reassure her and, interested, urged her to continue. Lighting a cigarette, she deliberately blew a long spiral of smoke, watching it rise into the leaves of the sycamore.

'I was surprised,' she began, 'to see how much of the whisky I had drunk when I took it from the bag, deciding there was enough to last me until the evening. You know, the days seemed to drag, I tried so hard not to think too much.'

She stood up, straightening her skirt and brushing off the grey powdery ash before sitting down again. In the sunlight she looked beautiful, now that her eyes had lost their puffiness. Lighting another cigarette, she went on. 'Looking inside my bag I came across a canvas package which I knew didn't belong to me. How it got there I just don't know.' I remembered the package in the oak and explained how I had picked it up, assuming it belonged to her. She looked at me for a brief second before continuing.

'Well I never – let me tell you what was inside. You know, I had a strange feeling about it, I don't know why – remember I was so unhappy and confused. Inside I found a bible and a bundle of rough notes; in fact they were drafts of sermons. I left them on the table while I made myself a coffee, and when I returned to the room a shaft of bright sunlight was shining right on to the bible. It was uncanny and, at the same time, very beautiful. A peculiar feeling went through me – it passed right down to my toes. I felt I had experienced something very wonderful, it was most odd. I derived great comfort from the readings, although I must tell you I have never been what you might call a religious person. Anyway, I certainly did a lot of thinking. In fact so much, I never did drink the remainder of the whisky.'

Her eyes shone as she related the story.

'I still feel sadness, but at least I've managed to come to terms with it and I am off the bottle. Thank you for putting that in my bag – my life is on the mend.'

12

The Twins

A week of heavy, continuous rain had not only soothed the parched July countryside, but had encouraged the run of salmon coming in from the channel.

Standing on the bridge of the fertile river that meanders through the spectacular Teign valley of south Devon, I made an inspection of the fish-pass. The spate had now subsided, with the river down to a steady flow and deep water – excellent for the migratory trout, enabling them to travel to the upper reaches. July is the month when the peal (sea-trout) run reaches its peak and with it, of course, comes the inevitable increase in poaching.

Leaning over the rough granite ledge of the bridge, I watched a salmon attempting to jump the pass, when a voice enquired as to what was capturing my interest. I was looking through my field-glasses to see if the fish was diseased or not and, turning, discovered that the voice belonged to an elderly, pale-faced man whom I reasoned was a visitor from up-country. He was, in fact, from London and most eager for conversation. This was the second week of his holiday and he was staying at the small hotel which overlooked the ancient fish-pass, and for the next ten minutes or so he rambled on about the places he had visited. From what he said I could tell he was very observant, one of life's Nosy Parkers, who probed and ferreted out every possible situation and person.

Water bailiffs often pick up useful information through being good listeners; even so, enough is enough. I was about to make my departure when I stopped dead in my tracks. His last comment had touched a hidden memory; although I couldn't quite place what he was saying, I knew something was familiar about the description he gave of a recent observation he had made by the bridge.

During the latter part of the chat he had extolled the virtues of the hard-working, enterprising Devonians, marvelling at the patient, laborious passage that two young men were making as they man-handled a large milk churn across the field adjoining the river on the other side of the bridge.

'Surely,' he ventured, 'I would have thought that they would have used a tractor for such heavy work, especially as the field was soggy.' I pressed him to tell me more, without giving him the impression that I was unduly interested, remarking that perhaps it was a one-off occasion. He went on, explaining that it was just after daybreak yesterday.

'I was up early, having decided to take a short stroll before breakfast; the air down here is really something, different from where I come from, you know.' Agreeing, I urged him to continue.

He had watched the young fellows; they were half-way to the gate of the field, dragging and half lifting the tall silver churn to the road. 'I saw that they must be twins; actually, one of them stuttered badly.'

'So you spoke to them, then?'

'No – not really. I wished them good morning, asking if they had been milking.'

'What did they say?'

'One of them said aloud, "fer-fer-fer-g milking, you ca-ca-can say that again," as they put the churn into the car. It's a wonder the milk didn't come out, I certainly wouldn't have liked that in my car.'

Thanking him, I crossed the road and entered the gate, walking downstream and examining the bank as I went.

About five hundred yards from the bridge the river makes a gentle bend where a deep pool affords excellent cover among the roots of the oaks that fringe the river, some of them hundreds of years old. The exposed roots form dark caverns that are ideal for resting fish; it is an area of exquisite beauty. Here the river is quiet, just a gentle surge until about a quarter of a mile downstream where it explodes over the boulder-strewn bed, worn smooth as velvet by the constant wash over the years. The banks are covered in celandine, lady's smock, campion and tall, stately cow-parsley. It is also the home of the otter, heron and kingfisher that are secretly watched by fallow deer from the densely wooded hillside. Stone Age man lived and fished the river; the spot is evocative of the distant past and is one of utter tranquillity. You can even hear yourself think, and the silence is both therapeutic and comforting.

Noticing an area of buttercups that was squashed and flattened, I made a closer inspection; it revealed tell-tale evidence of poaching – the presence of fish scales and slime were recent. Collecting some for forensic, I investigated further, finding conclusive evidence that a net had been placed across the river at that point; it was more than likely that the milk churn had been used to transport the illegal catch. What a perfect ploy to use a rural container to allay suspicion, as was proved by the recent observation.

My report to HQ was received with interest, as the description of the two tallied with known poachers that hitherto had been active in Cornwall and were known as persistent offenders. With the river still running at poaching level, it was probable that they would be back to take advantage while the flow was reasonably high. There was no time to lose, as I was convinced they would be back that night, when we would be waiting.

The night was warm and balmy, smelling of dank soil and wild honeysuckle and, apart from the odd cloud, the moon shone continuously, presenting problems as we tried to conceal ourselves. Two bailiffs were on the true right bank (facing downstream), which was ideally covered in broad-leafed trees, affording a splendid lookout from the hillside, while we two were on the opposite bank with little cover in the open meadow. Thankfully the grass, although damp, was long, so we lay flat out and occasionally popped our heads up. We kept in touch by radio; however, it was vital to limit its use to reduce the likelihood of detection.

Further up river by the bridge, the sounds of revelry came drifting over the water from the hotel; we lay still, not daring to smoke or move about. After a while, my colleague whispered that he wished to relieve himself of the effects of an unwise pint of beer he had consumed before commencing the surveillance. I advised him to slide a few yards away and, without standing, perform the necessary manoeuvre and then return to his position. A matter of minutes later I heard stifled oaths, and assumed that the operation had not been too successful. The laboured return and damp trouser leg bore witness to the difficulty of this horizontal, nocturnal exercise.

My watch, which I could read without any trouble in the moonlight, showed a quarter to midnight, my legs were going into cramp, and I felt I must move them or I would go mad. Rubbing and shaking them brought a little relief, but my companion hissed at me to pipe down; he then had the audacity to say that he wanted a smoke. I promised to shoot him if he so much as thought about it, let alone put a cigarette in his mouth. Murmuring something uncomplimentary, he turned on his stomach, thrust his head on cupped hands and peered through the strands of coarse, yellowing grass. Apart from an occasional shout from a reveller, all was quiet from the hotel. An owl called from the hills; a loud flapping of wings from a disturbed wood-pigeon was magnified in the still night air.

A light mist was now drifting along the stretch of river. The night wore on with agonising slowness; all of us were by now starting to feel the effects of the cramped conditions. For a brief moment we thought we heard movements a little way off the river – it was a lumbering badger on its nightly foraging. Once again, we settled down for a long wait.

No sounds came from the hotel now; I imagined all the revellers tucked up in comfortable beds with real soft pillows and white sheets. I spoke softly to my partner, who seemed to be breathing deeply with a regular beat; I received no answer. I suspected that he must be dozing and, crawling my way over, a matter of some ten yards, I saw that his eyes were closed, and his mouth opened to the night air. I shook him by the ear and he gave a convulsive stir, closed his mouth and opened one eye which stared up at me, slurring, 'Wassa matter?' Angrily, I hissed my displeasure, returning to my position. The movement had eased my legs.

At precisely one-twenty, in the light of the moon, I could not only hear but also see the shadowy outline of a vehicle stopping by the field gate. My companion became alert; very softly, I relayed the information – message received and understood. The adrenalin began to flow, every sense was poised, a slight trembling of the body signalled the expected action; my mouth became dry, and my eyes were glued to the glasses pointed at the gate.

'For God's sake – make a move,' I murmured. Two men alighted carrying a couple of bundles, and quietly entered the field on their way to the water's edge. We could hear the swishing sound of the grass brushing against the bulky packages that were being half carried, half dragged by the men. The routine was to allow the net to be set, which would entail the use of an inflatable – in nearly all incidents it would be a small child's float that could be purchased practically anywhere. We would then pounce.

We watched as the men began to inflate the tiny orange-coloured float; not a word was spoken by either of them as they worked with practised ease and expertise. One of the men began to slip the float into the water, when he stopped abruptly. He was joined by his mate, and a whispered word passed between them as the two peered across the river up to the trees. Had they seen something? Were they deciding the best anchorage for the net? One pointed to the spot where the other bailiffs were hiding; they were uneasy! A message came over the radio from the head bailiff:, 'I believe we've been spotted, break cover and apprehend, we'll make our way to the vehicle – out!'

We rose stiffly and ran towards the poachers; we had definitely been spotted as they fled towards the gate, leaving behind the net and float. I closed with one of them, who jabbed a short stick into my stomach with such force that I dropped like a stone, completely winded. My mate shouted, 'All right?' But I could not answer; I just raised my arm half-heartedly. The two poachers succeeded in getting away completely. All of us were livid, and disappointed. We returned home in the early hours dispirited with our failure, blaming ourselves for our carelessness.

It took a little time to get over that night's escapade. Although we kept watch for the next two days, until the river had subsided enough to make netting virtually impossible, they never returned. I was determined that one day I would repay the jab I had received; the poacher's face remained imprinted on my memory. It was one of the notorious twins who had delivered the ultimate insult – and he was going to pay in full.

The summer wore on, with routine patrols and some successful night operations, although still no reports of the 'terrible twins'. Apparently they had gone to ground, though in no way, I suspected, because of our previous encounter. They were far too dedicated to allow that minor skirmish to deter them from their lucrative hobby.

The Twins

It was towards the end of September and we had just come in from a coastal patrol having spent a glorious day patrolling off the coast in a calm swell that made our trip pleasant and without incident. The Devon coast looked very beautiful from our tiny craft, and a few late holidaymakers still lingered on the various beaches and coves as we made our way into the tiny harbour. Both of us were tired and thirsty, and looking forward to a beer before going off duty. The pub we chose was a small, one-bar, rickety building that snuggled in between a boatyard and a small jetty, frequented by salmon netsmen.

As we entered the low-ceilinged bar, a couple of local fishermen looked up from their dominoes and said to the assembled drinkers – there were at least another six netsmen present – 'Watch out boys – they're about. Landlord, give the poor buggers a pint.' The elder of the two tossed a note over to the counter. We were not only used to the good-natured banter, but enjoyed it; we were old friends of these tough old salts.

'Cheers!' we wished the old mariner, who laughingly retorted, 'Hope it chokes you!'

'How's the fishing been, Tom?' I asked the younger of the two.

He grimaced, shaking his head. 'Not all that bright, you could say – struggling.'

He held his empty glass in front of me, giving a knowing look. I took the hint, refilling both of their glasses with strong ale. The ancient one leaned over to us in conspiratorial intimacy, saying in a semi-stage whisper, 'We know someone who is doing bloody well though, don't we Tom?' Tom nodded, taking a long swig at his beer; I could see at least one of his eyes staring at me, awaiting my expected response. My colleague rose and walked over to the bar where a Dutch seaman was making laboured enquiries of the landlord. I managed to catch the end of the exchange: 'Vot is 'er number?'

'Four drops of Navy, please.' My fellow bailiff returned placing the rum in front of us. The netsman drank our health.

Slowly and deliberately the old salt rolled a shag cigarette, appearing to enjoy the suspense. Dispensing with the spent match, he slowly broke it in two on the tatty ashtray; his eyes remained fixed to it as he spoke.

'Old Charlie down at the fish shop was offered four salmon cheap the other day, but he smelt a rat and refused the offer,' he said to us. 'I thought you said salmon was scarce – someone knows where to find them.' He changed the conversation, and I noticed that the other men in the bar were listening. We finished our drinks and bade them goodbye, leaving the pub with ribald comments ringing in our ears.

I made enquiries at the fishmongers, and he was most helpful and friendly; as he put it, 'You boys do a good job, you.' There was no doubt at all who were the sellers of the salmon.

'They looked like brothers, one poor bugger stammered badly and they both looked as though they could have done with some sleep. I told them I never touched that kind of business,' he volunteered.

'Did you see what kind of vehicle they had?' I asked.

'No – no business of mine – you.'

Thanking him, I left for HQ with the information. All bailiffs keep a written record of suspects' car numbers which are forever being updated; although the twins' vehicle registration was a year old, we hoped it hadn't been changed. At least we knew they were still active in our area, and I was determined to catch them. Little did I know that it was going to happen in a most unexpected way.

The fourth of October was absolutely foul: the rain simply fell in buckets, our first good fall in weeks, and a chilly north-easterly blew through the willows, scattering the leaves like confetti. My mate and I decided to pay a long overdue visit to a farmer friend, whose farm lay on a hill overlooking a back water of the river that skirted a large quarry. He was, in fact, an honorary bailiff, a most useful chap. In order to reach the house it was necessary to travel a small, narrow lane that wound very close to the water, and the rain was still falling as we drove slowly along it.

At the end, a gate led up to the farmhouse. Not many use the road apart from farmers; it was lonely and remote. After travelling about half the length of the lane my companion, who was looking out of the window, touched my arm, telling me to stop.

'There's a bloody net there!' He motioned to an old sycamore, where red binding cord was made fast; sure enough, there was a net strung across the river, a distance of twenty feet. The river was beginning to rise slowly as the rain came off the moor, causing the net to belly and strain against the flow.

Quickly hiding our car, we returned suitably dressed for a long wait. For a change, luck was with us that day, for no sooner had we concealed ourselves among the rocks than a car splashed to a stop. With complete self-assurance, two men walked towards the net not yards from the lane, each wearing a bright yellow oilskin with the letters of some rural council on the back of the jackets – another ploy to allay the suspicion of the onlooker. They both began to loosen the cord, while a third man had appeared on the opposite bank carrying an inflated float. This time we must not fail; the suddenness of attack took them completely by surprise. We both grabbed one man, allowing the other two to escape, and this time I did not let go. When the oilskin was removed – surprise, surprise! It was indeed our friend, who had given me the wicked jab on that fateful night! I was delighted. We were astonished that neither of the other men attempted a rescue as the offender was frogmarched back to the farm. Progress was fitful, as we kept falling over the rocks with the prisoner – those granite lumps do hurt!

The twins were successfully prosecuted and their gear confiscated, but latest intelligence is that both are still working the rivers all over the county.

Any suggestions? Like prostitution, poaching I fear will remain with us to the very end of time!

13
Chasing Rainbows

Benjamin Claudius Bentwhistle was a kindly little man. His slight build was always covered in a huge oilskin jacket, with a pair of waders that looked as if they reached to his very armpits, while his fishing rod towered above his soft, baby face. The white hair, what was left of it, fringing his crown can only be described as thistledown. Perched on his pert nose, a pair of gold half-moon spectacles gave him an air of a Jules Verne absent-minded professor. Laughter lines around the corners of his grey eyes told of the many jolly encounters that he had experienced in his sixty-three years. He was, by profession, a scientist in the employ of HM Research Establishment. A boffin indeed!

I first met Ben two years ago, when he came to fish my waters. While on patrol of my lake I had assisted in the removal of a 'Zulu' fly from his ear, and we had been friends ever since. I cannot say that he had been a successful angler; to my knowledge over those two years he only managed to capture two tiny brown trout, and even then I heard tell that these were netted in the shallows. However, I felt compassion for this inoffensive little man.

Regularly, once a week, Ben could be seen casting fly after fly to the unseen trout, only to have, after several hours, extremely tired arms, several lost flies and an empty cigarette packet. Often at his spot I had counted eighteen cigarette ends and enough spent matches to shame a woodyard. But I must say he persisted, and remained calm and happy. Then his luck seemed to change overnight.

Ben had confided to me that from now on he was going to fish from a boat, where perhaps he would be more successful – and indeed he was. On every visit from then on he caught his limit, and what's more, he had taken to visiting all the reservoirs that had boats – with the same results! Soon, this little man became known as the expert angler, and fishing correspondents sought his story, only to be met with a bland smile and non-committal answers.

It was a perfect day for fishing: the August sky gave cloud cover, the fresh southerly produced a magnificent ripple, and all around the trout were taking fly. The time was ten-thirty in the morning as I began my boat patrol; there were not many anglers on the banks and only two boats were out, one containing Benjamin Claudius. I had always given him a wide berth in the past, but now I was a little curious. Standing off from his boat, I observed Ben fishing happily; in his ears he had a pair of plugs, which I assume was attached to a radio. He was gaily nodding his head as though in time to silent music. I raised a hand in salute and he smiled back, holding one finger up to denote his first rainbow trout. He looked a picture of contentment as I left him.

Now, the odd thing was that when the fishing was poor, Ben would always manage to secure his limit bag. Other bailiffs began to remark on this eccentric character, who had confessed to being very fond of Debussy, besides fishing. 'It helps me to relax,' he would say – and apparently to catch fish, I would have said.

September arrived in all her magic, the air was still warm, and there was superb cloud cover and enough breeze off the moor to produce a tantalising ripple. Most of the visitors had departed to the big cities, leaving the big expanse of trout-filled waters to the natives. As usual, the professor arrived with his tackle for another day's fishing, but I noticed that his pace was slower and that he had a tired look about his eyes. He assured me he was well, but asked if I could give him a push out with his boat. I gladly obliged.

About half-past eleven an angler came into the office to weigh his catch, and after a chat he remarked that 'our friend' the professor was sleeping on the bankside. To my knowledge, he had never done this before and I remarked that he was obviously feeling his age now, dismissing the incident from my mind. My boat patrol commenced at half-past four, and on rounding the bay I saw Ben's boat just drifting offshore – empty. As I closed, I could see him still sleeping, so I took his craft in tow and made for the bank.

It did not take me long to discover that he was not asleep, but dead. There was a smile on his face as the September breeze ruffled his hair, and alongside him were his ear-plugs. I could imagine him going to sleep listening to his beloved music. What a perfect way to go.

The ambulance arrived and Benjamin Claudius was taken gently away. I gave his three fish to the driver, as they would otherwise be thrown away. Packing his gear together I gradually became puzzled, firstly that there was no sign of a

radio at all, and secondly, that on the tip of his rod was a small disc, in fact like a spy bug, which had been incorporated in the rod. I had certainly never seen anything like this before. I then came across a large metal box that was obviously his lunch container, and when I opened it – trout pellets by the pound. Oh dear! I know that this goes on in lots of trout fisheries and is difficult to check, but I made my report all the same and notified HQ.

Two days later the telephone rang. Apparently the ambulance driver had handed the fish that I had given him to his wife, who was an assistant in the X-ray department. She had placed the trout on a nearby table to be taken home later. The radiologist had then come into the room and from her detector had picked up tell-tale signals from the bag of rainbows, announcing them to be radioactive.

After weeks of enquiries, a picture was formed of how our dear man had become a successful fisherman. At the research laboratory, Ben had managed to mix trout pellets with radioactive dust and devise a very clever detector. He would feed the pellets over a selected area and then fish in the conventional manner, picking up the movements from his rod while receiving the signals via the ear-plugs.

I have no doubt at all that most of the fish in the county's reservoirs are suffering from hiccups, although we have been told on good authority that the radioactive rainbows are harmless.

Now I know why Ben had a smile on his face! What is it that Dr Johnson said? 'Fly fishing may be a very pleasant amusement; but angling or float fishing I can only compare to a stick and a string, with a worm at one end, and a fool at the other.'

14

The Miracle

Monday was his day of complete anonymity: false teeth in pocket, old fishing hat decorated with coloured flies, old trousers, old jacket, old waders and an old, well-used rod. In fact, it looked as if he had gone to great lengths to disguise his very well-being. Nobody would even guess that yesterday he had been host to royalty.

He walked at a leisurely pace along the bank until he reached his favourite spot, a finger of heather-clad bank that reached out into the water at the entrance to the bay; a lonely place, shared only with the heron. But it was here that the Bishop found absolute relaxation. In fact, it had become known, unofficially, as 'Bishop's Ripple'.

Placing his rod and tackle against a lichen-covered boulder, he slowly filled his pipe; that, too, was old.

'This is heaven,' he mused.

The sky was overcast, with a steady ripple on the water; perfect conditions, and what's more, the fish were rising to the 'alders'.

'Hmm,' he thought, 'with a bit of luck I might take a trout.' A modest man, an excellent fisherman; none of the big, ugly lures on the bottom, but a dry fly on the surface all the time, and a small one at that!

His previous week had been busy. Several meetings, services, a marriage and of course the highlight of the week, the visit by royalty. So today was going to be a day of relaxation. A friendly goose paddled up alongside as he sat puffing his pipe before commencing casting a fly. Searching his pocket, he found a forgotten biscuit; a bit soft, but it would do. He was continually being scolded by his wife for leaving 'debris', as she put it, in his pockets. 'Quentin,'

The Miracle

she would scold, 'really, you should burn these smelly old clothes – and the pieces of food I find – really!' He would smile patiently, telling her not to fuss.

He was one of the kindest men I have ever met. In his middle fifties, inclined to be plump, of medium height and with a shock of silver hair which framed his cherub face, the blue eyes shone out from clear, pink skin: the epitome of a man of God.

I had decided to do a boat patrol during the late afternoon. The lake was well attended, and a word here and there took care of the hour. Soon I reached the spot where the Bishop was fishing but decided not to disturb him, making my way well out into the middle of the lake. Travelling at low speed so as not to disturb the fish, as I reached abaft of him I raised my hand in salute, and he beckoned me to come alongside. Sitting at the water's edge thoughtfully sucking his pipe, he pointed to a freshly landed rainbow trout of about two pounds.

'Robert, come and look at this – extraordinary!'

I examined the fish. On its side was a mutation – a distinct sign of a cross. It extended down the lateral line of the trout, looking just as if it had been painted. I was astonished; the Bishop, I could see, was deep in thought. 'Truly amazing, Robert,' he murmured gently. I quietly left him and continued my patrol.

During the early evening I was talking to a disappointed angler who had been fishing most of the day without success. He told me that he wanted to catch a little fish for his wife, who was very ill. I sympathised with him, wondering how I could help, when into the office strode the Bishop looking very pleased with himself. He had caught his limit of five rainbows, which he had weighed for his records.

'Hello John, any luck today?' greeted the Bishop.

'No sir, just not my day, I've had a couple on but lost them. Mary will be disappointed,' replied John.

'How is she?' The Bishop knew the family.

'Up and down sir, it's a bit hard, you know.'

From his bag the Bishop reached for a fish. 'Look here, give her this, with my best wishes.'

John was beside himself with thanks. As he left, the

man of God reminded me that he was off to Scotland for the next three weeks to fish the lochs. I bade him good fishing.

It was a month later when I next saw John, looking a changed man. 'Good morning John, how's the wife?'

John looked at me with moist eyes. 'It's a miracle, the doctors are puzzled, she is on the mend. Never seen such a change in a person. You know, doctors are wonderful people.'

I left him fishing, he was at peace now.

The Bishop came fishing the next week, and we exchanged

news; apparently he had an excellent and fruitful holiday, with a ten-pound salmon to prove it.

'Hope you've stocked the waters since I've been gone Robert.' I reassured him. 'By the way,' he called out as I was about to leave, 'when I last fished, remember that rainbow trout with the mutation?'

'Yes,' I replied.

'Well, when I arrived at the palace I went to show it to my wife, but to my dismay, I found that I must have given it to John. A pity really, the Archbishop was coming on a visit and I would have liked him to have seen it.'

I retraced my footsteps until I was close to him. Looking him straight in the eye, I said, 'My Lord Bishop, may I humbly suggest when you get back to the palace you read Jeremiah 30:17: "For I will restore health unto thee, and I will heal thee of thy wounds, saith the Lord".'

15

Wee, Wee!

I am sure you can remember as a child dressing up: the girls in their mother's dresses trailing the floor, the tottering of high heels elevating to grown-up stature, the dangling earrings from beneath a wide-brimmed bonnet framing vermilion-smudged lips; the boy's heads eclipsed with an assortment of father's hats – bowlers, always the favourite, flat caps or maybe a real relic from the past, a straw boater retrieved from a dusty attic – concertinaed trousers capable of holding a sack of potatoes in the generous-sized bottom, and not forgetting, of course, a borrowed pipe from dad's cherished collection.

All of us at sometime or another have indulged in the fantasy of impatient maturity, longing for the day when we can leave our childhood behind; alas, in the later years to yearn once more for those carefree days of youth. It is like, I suppose, a black man longing for a paler skin, while a white man goes to extraordinary lengths and expense to acquire a deep tan. There is no doubt at all, the grass is greener on the other side – or is it?

At the age of forty, Freddie Payne had never quite left the world of fantasy: the uncontrollable urge to masquerade remained with him well into middle age; until, that is, he attempted to make it pay. Freddie was, without a doubt, a real-life Walter Mitty.

June arrived on Dartmoor with magnificent splendour: the sun shone continuously, and was followed by long, balmy nights with prolific hatches of sedge that encouraged anglers to linger on the waters way past the permitted closing time. Everyone seemed to be enjoying life in this wonderland of green fields and high hedges, fertile rivers and inland lakes teeming with prime rainbow trout – paradise!

Wee, Wee!

At ten on the first of such mornings, Frederick Payne Esq. arrived at the permit office, smiling, oozing bonhomie and speaking with an exaggerated American drawl. He was wearing a white ten-gallon hat, Dallas style, a safari suit with a boot-lace tie and his tanned throat and he looked as if he had just stepped off a Mississippi river steamer. I was even tempted to look out of the window to see if, in fact, there was such a craft alongside.

'Hi there! I guess you must be the "boss-man" around here,' he drawled, taking from his shirt pocket a genuine packet of Camel cigarettes and expertly flicking one into the corner of his mouth. Blowing a spiral of scented smoke across the office, he continued, 'Sure looks kinda pretty out there,' waving his arm towards the water, 'what kinda fish swim here?'

I must confess that this flamboyant character was the genuine article. I went to some lengths to explain, and to advise him as to the best fishing methods, species of trout, and so on. He listened intently, punctuating my advice with comments such as, 'Sure', 'Is that right?' and 'Gee, that's mighty fine', but for most of the time just 'Yep!'

He wrote his name as 'Chuck Brodie, Montana, USA' on the permit and held out his palm to me with a handful of assorted coins, inviting me to take the fee. 'Just can't get the hang of this dang toy money.'

I quickly reminded him that in no way was this, as he so called it, toy money, and that this country had had a currency long before the mighty US of A was ever thought of! You may think I over-reacted, but the sheer arrogance and general demeanour of this tall, cowboy-like man was beginning to get under my skin.

He laughed outright when I told him the average weight of the fish was a pound and a half. 'Say bud, back home in the States we toss 'em back at four pounds,' he bragged. I held myself in check, treating him with laboured courtesy; he was, I could see, going to upset a lot of my staid anglers, who sought the sanctuary of the lake for peace and quiet. He left the office for the car park amidst raised eyebrows and smiles from arriving fishermen.

I began my patrol of the reservoir after lunch, spending

107

a few minutes with anglers who were having a pleasant, carefree day on the waters. Some had seen and spoken with our 'cousin' from across the Atlantic, and had been regaled with tales of the magnificence of fishing in America. The Bishop, a wise, well-travelled man, expressed doubts as to the authenticity of our colourful character, who was at this very moment casting a fly a few hundred feet away into the bay.

'Robert, I suggest you treat him with a pinch of salt. By the way, I've caught a nice one here,' he said, inviting me to look at the freshly caught rainbow; it was, I suppose, a

good three pounds in weight. I thanked him for the advice and continued on my patrol.

Before I had reached the bay, our friend had spotted me; putting his rod on the bank, he lit up a cigarette and appeared to be waiting for me. Perhaps I was about to be given a talk on the wonders of the 'big country'. He watched every step I took as I drew nearer; waving a greeting like a long-lost friend, he shouted, 'Hi there!' patting the grass alongside him. 'Have a Camel.'

I noticed as I sat down that his fishing tackle was all British and enquired if he had in fact hired it, although I could see that the gear had been well used. Somehow, it looked as if they were old friends.

'No – I have a buddy over here where I'm staying, he has an outfit over Crediton. I come over to England every now and again to get some of your Devon Reds for my stock. Fancy a slug of rye?' He reached for a half bottle of whisky from his bag.

He seemed reluctant to let me leave, attempting to strike up a conversation about the magnitude of his 'spread' back over the other side. The ten-gallon hat lay on the bank; it had been hooked, and a 'Bloody Butcher' fly clung to the crown. I politely suggested that if he intended to spend more time at the lake he would be well advised to dress more suitably. His present attire was, I thought, more in keeping with 'mint juleps' on some spacious lawn. He laughed heartily at that. 'Gee you're some guy!' he remarked as I took my leave of him.

A month was to pass before I was to meet him again, in a very different guise. A colleague and I were doing a river patrol; the going had been tough over rocky terrain, the sun beat down mercilessly and we both were very thirsty, just gasping for a refreshing drink. Dartmoor was packed with holidaymakers, all taking advantage of our fickle weather, and my companion suggested we call on the way home for a drink at the inn that perched high on the moor. As was to be expected, as we drew nearer to the pub we saw several visitors milling around outside on the grass drinking and eating, and generally indulging in merriment. Parking my car on the grass verge, my friend went to purchase a couple of pints.

At one of the picnic tables outside, a small group of visitors sat laughing and listening to a vaguely familiar face. The speaker emphasised his tales with elaborate gesticulations, and his audience seemed spellbound by his oratory. I could see my colleague weaving his way back through the crowds, gingerly carrying two pints of bitter that looked most inviting in the sunshine.

He stopped momentarily by the table where the man was holding court, at the same time taking a swig from each glass to prevent spillage and listening to the speaker, who was dressed in a flowered short-sleeved shirt, a red-and-white spotted neck-scarf at his throat. The black béret, favoured by French onion-sellers, looked impressive, while the open sandals were sockless. To me he was a typical theatrical Frenchman, waving his arms at each remark, and much so that the gold earring he wore swung like a pendulum. A colourful, entertaining fellow indeed, out here on the open expanse of moorland.

We both took a long draught from the tall glasses – it was delicious. Pointing to the table with a nod of his head, my companion said, 'He's some character, they're keeping him supplied with plenty of booze. His accent is fascinating – like Maurice Chevalier, a typical romantic Frenchman – the girls are lapping him up.' There was certainly something familiar about his bearing: perhaps, I reasoned, he reminded me of one of the hundreds of anglers that I meet during the year. However, the thin pencil moustache he was wearing confused me.

I collected the two empty glasses and left for the bar, determined to get a clearer view of the entertainer. He was in full view as I neared the table; I gave him a quizzical look, and for a brief moment I swear I made him falter, as if he recognised me. However, he quickly composed himself and resumed his tales.

As I collected the beer from the bar, a wicked thought went through my head: I played a hunch, deciding I would air my schoolboy French on him on my return. Wishing him good day, I asked him what part of France he was from – hoping to God I would be able to understand his reply.

The effect was remarkable: his audience looked up at

me, smiling, while he hesitantly searched for an answer. I repeated my question, suggesting Calais; he shrugged his shoulders and replied, 'Wee, Wee!' with the emphasis on the 'W'. I knew then that this man was a fraud, and must surely be the 'cowboy' I had met earlier last month.

I discreetly moved away towards my fellow bailiff, who asked me what all that had been about. When I had told him about my previous encounter and suspicions, he replied, 'The man's obviously a nutcase.' Before we had finished our drinks, the 'Frenchman' had left, driving away in an old Morris Minor; however, we noted the registration number.

So what, maybe I can hear you say, he hadn't caused you any harm; perhaps he is just some kind of harmless fool. True, but these characters sometimes develop a nasty habit of relieving folk of their possessions and the like. In our line of work we are taught to be suspicious and to try to remain one jump ahead. Anyway, I was convinced that he was, in fact, the 'American'.

The summer drew to a close without a further sighting of our 'con artist', and he quickly became a memory. Up country, on the borders of the county, a huge new reservoir had been built, with several miles of water providing an excellent fishery, sailing and many enchanting walks around the acres. I was friendly with the bailiff who had taken command of this superb venue, and had promised to spend a day's fishing with him. There were a couple of weeks left before the fishing season closed and I was determined to take advantage of the good weather.

I drove through the early morning haze that invariably heralds a warm, dry day and was really looking forward to a change of scenery, having never visited the area before. The countryside looked beautiful with the trees beginning to change colour; most of the holidaymakers had left for the big cities and there was a peaceful atmosphere all around. On reaching high ground, beneath me in the distance the sparkling waters of the lake reached out invitingly. I drove into the large gravelled area where several cars were already parked, their occupants out on the banks or in boats, fishing. It was a scene of utter peace and tranquillity, and the only sound came from a blackbird singing to the morning sky.

111

My friend and I spent the next few minutes exchanging news, both looking forward to a good day's sport. I suppose it couldn't have been more than ten minutes before my friend was summoned outside to deal with an enquiry. He left me poring over some recent photographs and was gone some time; I was about to go and find him when he came in the door.

'Robert, I suppose you haven't a tenner on you until we get home, have you?'

I gave him the cash and he disappeared again saying he wouldn't be a couple of seconds. Within a minute he was back, and I prepared my tackle. The bailiff suggested that I hired a boat, and he would join me within half an hour. I walked to the jetty and chose a sleek new boat; a light breeze teased the water, and a couple of ducks moved forward, expecting a titbit.

Within seconds of casting I hooked a rainbow. What luck – I am not the best of fishermen and I was encouraged no end. I decided to pull further into the middle of the lake, where two boats were stationary; the anglers in them were fishing intently.

Nearing them, I could make out in one of the craft an individual wearing a blue baseball cap smothered in gold braid, like the ones favoured by astronauts which seem to be gaining popularity in this country. I suppose it gives the wearer a feeling of authority to wear the gold braid of a naval commander. However, this man was so completely engrossed in fishing that he never gave me so much as a glance – thankfully. There was no mistaking him this time: it was, as you have no doubt guessed, our friend from Montana!

Casually, I turned the boat and made for the shore, forcing myself not to appear as though I was hurrying, although I wanted to get out and run. Securing the dinghy alongside, I made towards the bailiff's house, but he was already half-way down the track all kitted up for fishing. Seeing me, he said, 'However did you know that I was ready? The last I saw of you you were mid-stream – that was good timing.' I asked him to sit down on the bank while I told him of my past encounters with the flamboyant Yank and the so-called Frenchman. His face was a picture.

'You don't know it, but that tenner was for *him*! Him wearing the gold braid!' He simply laughed, exclaiming, 'Good Lord!' My reply was unprintable!

We both hurried to the office to examine his permit. The address he had given was that of a local hotel, in the name of Fred Barnes. A telephone call to the hotel did, in fact, confirm that he was in residence, having booked in the previous night. The hotelier commented on the generosity of the man; he had entertained lavishly the previous evening, insisting that the cost was to go on his bill. We made no attempt to give the hotelier cause for suspicion and simply thanked him, inventing an excuse for the enquiry. We then searched the car park and luck was with us, for there parked among the other cars was the Morris Minor. A quick telephone call to the police informing them of our suspicions revealed that the keeper was, in fact, a Frederick Payne, and known to the police. I was pleased, looking forward to the confrontation, but the police advised us to do nothing.

The bailiff said that the man had told him that he was a factory owner from the Midlands staying at the local hotel. He had, so he said, left his wallet in his other jacket so my friend had, from his own pocket, advanced him the fishing fee and boat ticket, and he had requested a further ten pounds for petrol. He also explained that the old Morris was his hobby, and he had several other old cars in his collection. The bailiff explained that he was, as he thought, a nice fellow who had, in fact, invited him to an evening's entertainment at the hotel at his expense.

'Naturally, I was completely taken with him,' my friend explained. I asked him what accent he had used. 'Oh, typical Irish – he struck me as a rough diamond who had made good.'

At the request of the police, we played it cool.

Fishing that day was completely out of the question, so I remained with the bailiff to monitor results. I was indeed looking forward to meeting the 'con man' again, but thought it prudent to remain out of sight. He was bound to recognise me, which would blow the whole operation.

He eventually left the lake at four-thirty. I watched from the office window; there was no mistaking him this time.

Reluctantly , I left for home, ten pounds and my fishing fee lighter, having caught one rainbow – an expensive fish. The bailiff promised to keep me informed.

That same evening, at the request of the police, my friend attended the hotel, where he was entertained along with some other anglers.

The telephone rang at well past midnight, much to my wife's annoyance. I was told it was the hardest role my colleague had ever played.

'Did you manage to collect the loan?'

'No. He promised to repay the next day as soon as the bank opened.' We both knew that something wasn't quite right. I promised not to be out of earshot during the day, as I wanted to be kept informed of all the latest events.

At precisely ten in the morning the news came: the con man had left the hotel, saying he was going fishing at the reservoir once more. Instead, he sped hot-foot towards Bristol, where he was detained and questioned by the waiting police. In his flamboyant style, he confessed to not only one charge of deception but many others.

I am expecting to be summoned to appear in court at any moment to give evidence and, hopefully, recover my tenner. There is one thing of which I am sure, however, and that is that if I'm asked if I can recognise the defendant I shall most certainly reply: 'Wee, Wee!!!'

16

Sam

Sam Foggett stood on the balcony of his Victorian house, surveying his estate. His eyes took in the squat Bramley and Cox's Orange Pippin trees that were in full blossom; the half-acre orchard on the sloping ground was a blaze of pink and white, where families of blue tits searched feverishly among the bedecked branches. A little to the right lay another half acre of fertile ground which was devoted solely to tobacco: his ruling passion, his compulsive hobby. No matter what the time of day he could be seen sucking on his pipe like a fractious child, the carbon-encrusted bowl glowing like an Olympic torch.

Sam was an imposing figure, a shade under six foot, slightly built and with the sort of magnificent white, flowing beard that one associates with biblical characters in a Hollywood extravaganza. Although only in his fifties, he had retired from the north of England a wealthy man: he had made his fortune from scrap. Bluff, outspoken to the point of rudeness, he was a Yorkshireman who called a spade a bloody shovel. Years ago, as an impoverished married man, he had spent a brief holiday in Devon and it had left a lasting impression on him. So much so, in fact, that he was determined to return one day to spend his remaining years in the shadow of Dartmoor.

Although Sam could be described as a man who had everything – a devoted young wife many years his junior, a charming daughter, a gleaming Rolls that for most of the time remained in the garage – he had become restless and bored. It was on this spring morning, however, that his life was to change – just a little – and for a short time at least it would give him a chance to relieve his enforced inactivity.

Calling to his wife, Sam told her he was going fishing down at the river which ran close by, and he would be home later.

A cloud of pungent, evil-smelling smoke marked his passage along the river bank, which even the most persistent midge refused to penetrate. He chose a spot in a small clearing where he could cast his fly without too much difficulty; after all, he was a newcomer to this gentle art of fly fishing.

The 'March-Brown' settled on the water, travelling downstream with the current, as Sam sucked on his pipe and reflected on his past life among the tall, smoking chimneys of the Black Country. He barely noticed the river bailiff, who appeared as if by magic from the screen of willows, asking to inspect his licence. After the initial shock of the bailiff's presence, he produced the official slip of paper. Eager for company, Sam plied the bailiff with many questions concerning his duties and experiences, listening intently to the answers. He decided then and there that by hook or by crook he, too, was going to become a water bailiff, and when Sam Foggett made up his mind, that was that! In fact, he was already walking the rivers, enacting the role of water bailiff. Unfortunately, what he refused to acknowledge was that he suffered from a pathological fear of water, and being a bailiff does not mean that one simply walks the dry banks of a river all day long inspecting pieces of paper.

At that time the authority's policy was to engage mature men such as retired policemen and the like to be trained as bailiffs (today, of course, it is quite different). Sam Foggett duly presented himself to the authority and, his skill and tenacity being obvious, was given the promise of the next vacancy.

Over the next couple of months Sam tried hard to settle down to a spot of gardening and, of course, to his constant fiddling with his beloved tobacco plants – he did his own processing of the leaves, which subsequently produced the evil-smelling mixture. But still the burning desire to be a bailiff overrode everything and everybody. Many times his long-suffering wife begged him to show restraint, which only resulted in his storming out of the house and into the curing shed, where he sulked among the drying tobacco leaves. Even the Siamese cat gave him a wide berth on these occasions, having experienced the feel of his strong leather shoes.

At long last, one sunny August morning an official-looking envelope dropped on to the mat. Sam was in the village, remonstrating with the newsagent about the non-delivery of his morning newspaper – which happened regularly, owing to the fickleness of the delivery boys. The kindly Devonian shopkeeper placated his anger with a countryman's patience and humour, which resulted every time in Sam leaving the shop not really sure who had admonished whom.

Mrs Foggett picked up the letter and placed it on the mantelpiece, before returning to her kitchen where she was busily bottling fruit.

Sam stood framed at the French windows, the sun behind him, looking like Moses about to address the faithful. Being a practical man, he invariably entered the house from the back; it was simply quicker.

'Is that you, Samuel?' She always used his full name, regarding the shortened version as only suitable for a dog.

'Aye lass.'

'Look on the mantelpiece.'

After reading the contents Sam let out a yell of pleasure and promptly disappeared into the lavatory. That was the beginning of Mr Foggett as a potential water bailiff.

After initial training, Sam, in company with three experienced bailiffs, was sent to do a survey on the upper reaches of the river on Dartmoor. Unfortunately, a little while before the operation had begun he had met with an accident while mowing the grass in the orchard. The blades of the machine had been jammed with a twig, and Sam unwisely left the engine running while attempting to remove the obstruction. Inevitably, the blades took the top off his finger, so he promptly picked himself up and drove himself to the local cottage hospital.

Sam had left the hospital with a heavily bandaged finger that stood up like a signpost; by the time he arrived home he had several knocks and wasn't too happy (the cat could confirm that). However, he was a tough old bird, the injury never really bothered him and it was the sheer inconvenience

of the amount of bandage that forced him to walk around
with his finger looking like a miniature lance.

The fisheries officer had suggested that it would be more
prudent for Sam to remain at home until the wound
had healed, but his spirited protestations completely over-
whelmed the suggestion and he was permitted to accompany
the crew on the survey. 'I can hold the lead of the electrodes
anyway, can't I?' It was agreed that he should remain on the
river bank, feeding the long cables attached to the generator
to the two men who would electro-fish.

So, on this late summer's day the party set out in the
Land-Rover for an isolated area on the moor. Sam sat up in
front with the driver, holding his finger out of the window
as though accusing anyone and everyone of his plight.

By the time the party reached the site, Sam was visibly
moved by the sheer wilderness of this lonely, silent place.
Brian, a most experienced Dartmoor man, began to mark the
passage through the mire with small yellow flags to enable
the vehicle to proceed in safety to the site itself.

The survey got underway with practised ease. Sam suffered one or two painful knocks and was obviously in pain,
but he was determined not to show it, and simply bit more
tightly on the stem of his pipe. The rest of the men were
being troubled by clouds of biting midges; all, that is, except
Sam, whose head was invariably covered in a cloud of acrid
smoke. He seemed to be unaware of his good fortune as he
diligently tended to the long coil of lead.

By lunchtime the survey was almost practically complete; the men lit a small fire and soon egg and sausages
were sizzling, sending mouth-watering smells out over the
heather-clad wilderness. The Yorkshireman was really in
his element, enjoying the carefree life of the water bailiff,
although the time was to come when he was to be brought
down to earth – and that was in the not too distant future.

Towards late afternoon, as the equipment was being
loaded, Brian pointed to the distant tors. There, some fifteen
miles away, a rolling bank of mist was approaching, and it
certainly presented an awe-inspiring sight, like a gigantic,
moving wall. All the gear was loaded in record time, but
even so, the mist was nearly overhead by the time they

had finished. Brian decided to lead the rest through the way-marked area while they rode in the vehicle, but for some obscure reason Sam was adamant that in no way was he going to ride in the Land-Rover. 'Oh no, I'm walking,' he said, and began to walk away. By now visibility was less than six feet, and the party crawled after Brian's torch.

Samuel Foggett had completely vanished, but the party pressed on through the yellow, flagged channel. The mist was now moving faster than a man could walk, rolling in huge, damp clouds; no one would have chosen to be in this place right now, and apprehension was being shown

all round. After a while, a voice called out in anguish somewhere out there in the mist: 'Where are you – can you hear me?' It seemed to be some way off – but in what direction?

The engine of the motor was switched off and the hooter sounded at intervals as a beacon for the hard-headed Yorky. The team cursed, as they were eager to leave this inhospitable area quickly. After what seemed an age, the ghost-like apparition with dew-encrusted beard and protruding finger appeared through the mist, looking absolutely petrified. Suitably chastised, he retreated into the vehicle, sucking nervously on the glowing pipe, and causing the men to cough and splutter. One bailiff gave him a real blast for putting lives at risk and Sam looked like a little boy who had been caught stealing apples, apologising as he puffed all the more vigorously.

He arrived home strangely subdued. His wife enquired if he had had a good day, but he just muttered, 'I'm hungry and tired – I'm going to have a bath.'

Over the following weeks the finger healed, and Sam was able to settle down once more to learn more of his other duties. But one assignment he was sent on finally made him decide that he no longer wanted to be a water bailiff. Although it was a purely routine task and not considered hazardous, it was enough to terrify him, and all because of his fear of water. Surely he must have known that it was necessary for a bailiff to be completely involved with water one way or another, either in or out of the stuff?

The autumn frosts began to trigger the spawning instincts of the salmon, followed by a subsequent increase in poaching activities. The fish spawn in shallow, fast-moving streams, making them especially vulnerable to the wicked prongs of the poacher's tool.

Fred the estuary bailiff was due for retirement, a dear old boy whose manner was one of tranquil forbearance. He spent most of his time patrolling the estuary in his little sixteen-foot, clinker-built boat, which he had named *Mary Anne* after his late departed wife. The chug of the engine could often be heard at the mouth of the river, Fred sitting in the stern smoking his pipe and making daily patrols in and around the creeks and tiny islets. The fertile river abounded with salmon and peal (sea-trout).

It was important that some night patrols be made further up river, where the salmon rested in the deep pools during their arduous passage to the spawning beds. These were the obvious target for poachers, who were undoubtedly knowledgeable about the fish; the task of the bailiff was to search for illegal nets across the river. The head bailiff decided that Sam and Fred would be ideal companions for this nightly exercise: each could outsmoke the other. The two were detailed for APP (anti-poaching patrol).

The night was as 'dark as a cow's guts' as Fred put it; the men had made their separate ways to the moorings, both dressed in oilskins and sea-boots and, of course, carrying their pipes! Sam looked decidedly nervous as the little craft nosed out into the blackness of the river; Fred knew it like the back of his hand, and steered a straight course for the upper reaches. Sam sat in the tiny bows looking tense; the red glow of his pipe reflected his tiny clenched mouth.

What Fred hadn't told Sam was that it was necessary to pump out the boat from time to time, as it was past its prime. It was, in fact, partially rotten and due for renewal, and only on Fred's insistence had he been permitted to keep the boat in service until he retired. He didn't fancy breaking in a new craft, and anyway, what was another eight weeks? No, he would manage.

By the time they had travelled a couple of miles the boat was carrying a good four inches of water. Fred, however, would let it reach six inches or more before starting to pump. He wasn't worried – he knew his *Mary Anne*. During the trip up river, very little conversation took place – Fred was not the talkative type; in fact, he was a loner. Sam was the complete opposite, but being apprehensive of water tended to make him less loquacious, and the result was that after about a mile silence reigned in the little boat.

By the time the twinkling lights of the town could be seen Sam felt better, and he looked up with relief as they sailed under the town's stone bridge: he was safe. His apprehension fading, he became talkative once again, but Fred remained taciturn. The lights of the town soon vanished, and as they turned a bend in the river total blackness was again upon them, as they headed into 'bandit territory'. Here the river narrowed and was thickly wooded on both sides, affording excellent anchorage for nets and superb cover for poachers.

Sam once more became silent. His leg began to itch and he reached down to scratch the outside of his sea-boot, which of course is like scratching your head while wearing a bowler hat. His hand touched water; he probed deeper into the darkness until his arm registered a fair depth. His immediate reaction signalled an urgent visit to the lavatory, and he let out a frantic yell: 'We're bloody well sinking, lad!'

His cry would have scared away any would-be poachers for miles as it echoed across the dark expanse. The sudden flapping of wood-pigeons from the trees set up a chain reaction, and several ducks took off in noisy flight.

Fred calmly began pumping, assuring Sam that it was perfectly safe and urging him to quieten down. But it was like talking to a mad bull. Sam showed all the signs of positive alarm, and broke wind with disconcerting frequency.

'Put me ashore! On land! Anywhere! Put me on the bank! I'm ill! Do you hear?'

As he steered for the bank in the complete darkness, Fred could now tell that his colleague was truly demented. His behaviour had completely disturbed Fred's sense of direction, for the boat touched land very quickly. Sam bounded off and, by the sound of him, not a moment too soon. Fred continued his patrol up river with cool disdain.

Unfortunately Fred was completely unaware that during the uproar and panic he had in fact landed Sam on a tiny island in the middle of the river, home to a family of irate swans. Once again the night air echoed to the frantic cries of the reluctant mariner as he tried to make his escape, chased off by some very angry swans. Finding only water all around as he tried to peer through the blackness, his cries were those of real terror, and to make matters worse he had suffered an unfortunate accident in his cords.

His pipe acted as a beacon for Fred as he turned the boat into the flooding tide. A very sorry man indeed stepped somewhat gingerly into the bobbing craft; Fred said little, and insisted that he was not going to put him ashore again until they reached the moorings. The trip downstream was slow against the flow and was made in complete silence. There was no doubt about it, Fred was extremely annoyed.

As soon as the boat was secured, Sam, walking like a crab, got into his car and left without so much as a goodbye.

Fred filled in his report, ending with 'mission unable to be completed owing to a touch of dysentery by colleague'.

Sam tendered his resignation soon afterwards. Now if you are anywhere near Mortonhampstead you will see him among his beloved tobacco – well away from water!

17

The General

The General had been a keen and regular visitor to the lakes. As a fisherman I would say he was above average, invariably going home with a brace or two. Inclined to be a loner, and somewhat distant and aloof with his fellow anglers, nevertheless he was a gentleman of the first order. One would find him fishing at least twice a week; that is, apart from his yearly visit to Scotland, when he fished the rivers with his old comrade, the Brigadier.

General R. C. Hodgeman VC – that's the name I shall give him – had seen many years' service in India, during which he had gained the reputation of being an obstinate and most determined man – an empire builder. Although in his late seventies, he still managed to retain his upright, soldier-like bearing. Just a fraction under six foot, his face was covered in a mass of tiny red veins – his nose undoubtedly savoured many a 'chota peg' of choice malt. His iron-grey hair was cropped short, with a moustache that could be described as 'tailored by Savile Row'. His strong jaw was deeply set into his once broad shoulders, draped now in Donegal tweed, and his feet were encased in strong brown leather. He would never enter the water: 'Disturbs the fish!' he would growl. The capable hands looked more at home with a service .45 than his Palakona fishing rod.

But despite all this, ever since his encounter with the 'Admiral' he had become a changed man.

The 'Admiral' was the name the fisherman had given to a huge brown trout whose weight had been estimated at about twenty pounds. He had lived for a long time in Clampitt Bay and many rods had fished unsuccessfully for him – he presented the ultimate challenge of the waters. Many times

I had seen him take a fly only to spit it out, seemingly with contempt. He resembled a young porpoise as he cruised slowly around his beloved bay; I secretly hoped he was never caught.

The General had become completely obsessed with the big fish and at the crack of dawn, day after day, week after week, he could be seen casting fly after fly, always in the bay, completely disregarding the more easily caught stocked fish. I have never seen such dedication.

As the weeks went by he became very bad tempered; his normally compact tackle could now be seen scattered on

the bank, boxes of flies strewn in disorder. With nostrils flared like an impatient filly, he would utter obscenities as he endeavoured to entice the wily old trout. But still the 'Admiral' would cruise just out of range, as though challenging the army to catch him. I am certain that a kind of rapport developed between the crusty old warrior and the brownie.

The August sky took on the appearance of an angry bruise; a freshening wind from the south-west heralded a likely storm. The lake became a mass of tiny wavelets, and it was as if the entire body of water was boiling. The atmosphere seemed charged with an air of foreboding. I knew somehow that something dramatic was about to unfold.

As usual, the General was fishing Clampitt. By now he had become part of the bay, and nobody paid much attention to him, dismissing him as a silly old fool. I had reached the bay after completing half my afternoon patrol, and decided to rest for a while under a granite outcrop that shadowed the little stream trickling into the bay. Lighting a cigarette, I watched the General fish. A terrific splash, accompanied by a high-pitched screech of his line, told me that the brownie had accepted the fly. He'll soon shake that off, I thought, hadn't I seen it all before? However, five minutes gradually gave way to ten: the fish was on!

The General's face was a study; he had become very calm. I could see his jaw muscles flexing as he played the noble fish. The General was again at war. The bay had become the Khyber Pass. The fight lasted a full twenty minutes. I moved in alongside, reluctantly offering to net it for him, but was waved aside with a brusque 'I can manage!'

I retreated to a discreet distance. It had begun to rain, spotting the water as the 'Admiral' was being landed; a couple of inquisitive damselflies hovered above its head, as if bidding farewell. I watched with a feeling of sadness, for I had known this trout for a long time and had even fed it by hand.

And then a most strange thing happened.

The fisherman was about to give the *coup de grâce* when I saw him pause, looking into the trout's eyes. Without a word, he gently removed the fly and slipped the fish back into the water, muttering softly, 'Good luck Admiral, perhaps now I can fish in peace.'

The Admiral is still making a mockery of the anglers – that is, all except one. I have since seen the old soldier feeding the fish by hand. I pretend not to see. He is a different man now; he actually gives me a smile. Needless to say, he never mentions the Admiral. Neither do I.

18

Voodoo

The two weeks' break had been wonderfully relaxing, especially as the weather had been kind. I was due to report back to duty at seven in the morning on a rather cloudy but warm day, and was eager to resume my official responsibilities at the lakes. The bailiff who had taken my place was due to meet me at the permit office, and no doubt would have a lot to talk about. I hoped he had enjoyed a reasonably quiet two weeks, free from any of the hassle that I knew could occur at any time.

The waters had been well attended, judging by reports I had read in the local press, and catches had been excellent. It was just after six-thirty when I arrived to begin preparing the permit office for opening time at nine o'clock. Looking at the noticeboard, I saw that my colleague had stocked the waters the previous day; the number of trout that I could see rising over the fishery promised a good day's sport.

September is always a good month for anglers: soft sunshine, cloud cover, with perhaps the hint of a breeze coming off the moor always produced ideal conditions for the trout fishermen. By ten to seven I had finished preparing the office and went to the rails to survey the waters with my field-glasses, awaiting the arrival of the bailiff. About half a mile away, at the extreme north end of the reservoir, people were fishing. The fishery was not officially open, which meant they were poachers. The area is remote and lonely, and from previous experience I knew that poachers chose that end to fish as the waters are literally surrounded by dense woodland, ensuring a quick escape.

I got into my car to meet my chum and to warn him of the intruders, and to set a plan in motion to apprehend the

128

law-breakers. The geese had sensed my presence, for they began to gather at the bankside where I normally fed them. I couldn't help feeling guilty as I set off along the narrow lane, stained with the scattered droppings of sheep that had recently moved from a nearby field.

I soon came across the bailiff, who skidded to a halt as we met head on. The lane was narrow, making it impossible for two vehicles to pass each other.

'What's the matter – did you think I wasn't coming?' he laughed. When I told him of my discovery, he exploded, 'On my last day too! Let's have the buggers!'

Leaving our cars a few hundred yards from the north entrance, we walked towards the small car park. It was empty, but in a little track off the lane we saw two vehicles hidden behind a lop-sided barn full of hay – a known spot that had been used in the past by poachers. We agreed that my colleague would conceal himself by the vehicles; luckily, he had brought his dog with him. We radioed the cars' registration numbers back to the head bailiff, who obtained valuable information from the police, who always are very co-operative.

Returning to the permit office, I parked my car and began to walk upstream to confront the early morning fishermen – I hoped! The half-mile walk through the tall, lank grass heavy with dew soaked my trousers within seconds. I could now see five men fishing, oblivious to my presence as I gradually closed in on them. I was now within yards of them, and noted that they were in their twenties, deeply tanned and athletic-looking. I reasoned that they were not from this country – just a hunch.

I radioed back a message that I was about to confront the poachers and needed assistance. My adrenalin was working overtime, as I fully expected to receive a bashing. To say I wasn't apprehensive would be a lie.

Trying to appear casual, I came closer to them, with my radio held in full view – the effect was magic! They ran towards the cover of the trees, vanishing out of sight. I took heart, making my way towards the other bailiff, whom I alerted to the situation. Seeing me, he broke cover, reporting that he had seen no one. They were obviously in the deep cover of pine. We prepared ourselves for a wait.

After a while two men, whom I recognised, came walking up the lane minus their rods and tackle, cheerfully bidding us good morning as they walked on; we were standing in full view of the cars. I called out for them to stop: they did so immediately. Both were sturdy and spoke with the clipped accent of the colonies. As we questioned them they both smiled, answering our enquiries with flippant arrogance, denying of course that they had been fishing.

'Are you the owners of these vehicles?' I asked.

'Yeese – we arr. We arr visitors exploring the countryside – so what?' The condescension was most pointed.

On the dashboard of one of the vehicles I had spotted a single fishing fly; on the ground beside the car I had picked up traces of nylon line, remnants of the tackling up. I advised them to call the other three or we would call the police dogs to flush them out, and said that it would make matters worse for them if they put us to all that trouble. I added that I recognised all of them, as they had been under observation. That did the trick: 'Fair enough,' they said and went into the woods.

Meanwhile, we received information on the keepers of the two cars, with names and addresses. They were students staying at a hostel in the nearby town.

We heard the two calling for their friends, and after a few minutes five healthy, tough-looking chaps carrying rods, and three brown trout, emerged laughing from the trees.

'Which of you is Mr A and Mr B?' I asked. They showed utter surprise at my knowing their names – the magic of radio!

It took a good half hour to question them and take statements. Giving them receipts for their gear, which we confiscated, we advised them to leave the area. The tackle amounted to over three hundred pounds' worth – all first class tackle. By the time we returned to the office it was well past nine, and several impatient anglers chided us with remarks such as 'What – overslept?' and the like. If only they knew!

That incident went off smoothly without any aggro, which

made a welcome change, I assure you. The five men were duly tried and fined, and because they had attempted no violence, it was agreed that the seized tackle should be returned to them. All were from sunny Africa. However, before the following summer arrived, I was to receive a threatening letter from one of them.

The tale was to have an unusual ending.

The remaining month of the season was purely routine. Bailiffs began preparing spawning maps of their rivers, ready for the annual search for the 'redds' (salmon nests) on the upper reaches of the rivers, always a critical time. It is of paramount importance to have a rough idea of the population of spawning fish – especially salmon – and, of course, close on the wake of spawning come the unscrupulous, violent poachers, who in this modern age make it a very lucrative pastime, unlike their forebears, who merely poached in order to enrich their diet. Long, cold nights spent in silent watch and sometimes ending in fierce confrontations were commonplace.

On magnificent starry nights, when Dartmoor lay silent in the grip of hard frost and the county lost in dreams, even the indifferent sheep, muffled in scraggy, unkempt coats touched with rime, sought the comfort of our presence in the bleak wilderness. How the inventor of the thermos has been blessed on these occasions when we were able to pour comforting hot drinks into our part-frozen bodies. Below us in the moonlit shadows salmon spawned in the ice-cold waters, a long way from the Atlantic rollers and a plentiful supply of food. A salmon lives only on its body fat while it is in the rivers; by the time it reaches the sea again it is weak and exhausted, and a proportion die after spawning.

During a rare, brief visit to HQ the fishery officer handed me a curiously addressed letter, remarking drily something about 'fan mail'. It bore the postmark of Cape Town; the address simply stated, 'The Bailiff, Fishing Reservoir, Dartmoor'. The ingenuity of the Post Office had ensured it reached me. In an elaborate, spidery scrawl, stained with, perhaps, red paint, the writer warned me that on his return to England he intended not only to poach enough fish to compensate for the cost of his fine, but also to extract one

131

half-pint of my English blood! I had visions of being attacked by a sunburnt poacher with a sackful of salmon, inserting a tap into my arm and filling a milk bottle full of my blood. Of course, although this kind of threat is rare, from experience I had learnt that we usually got trouble from poachers who remained silent.

This did mean, however, keeping a weather eye open for him; the sending of a threatening letter through HM mail was in itself an offence. The necessary precautions were taken.

With the explosion of welcome colour from the daffodils and primrose-studded banks, the fishing season began in earnest. The rivers and lakes echoed with the bow-string whine of the anglers' lines; gaily coloured flies and lures were cast on the warming waters; fishermen talked about last year's whoppers that always got away – this dedicated band of anglers rejoiced once again in the freedom of the banks after a long winter lay-off.

Birds were making frantic journeys to secret spots, their beaks stuffed with nesting material; stoats and ginger weasels stalked the heather for the unwary, gentle rabbits; geese sailed the water in pairs, while from the nearby fields came the incessant bleatings of lambs calling to their long-suffering mothers. Already visitors were arriving from the big cities, wandering aimlessly in and around the high-hedged lanes, dressed in the metallic yellow of celandine that brightens the Devon verges. From the cover of larch, a faint smudge of verdant green on the branches, the immature leaves softened the spiky twigs where squirrels sat, welcoming the new season.

Down by the bubbling feeder-stream, graced by tall rushes, all is quiet; a huge cottage-loaf boulder hides the heron who stands motionless, eyeing the water, head to one side as though listening to the sighing flow. A luxuriant growth of mosses carpets the narrow path leading to the main lake, where the trout constantly rise to the recent hatch of hawthorn flies. Rock-filled pools house thousands of darting tadpoles; the erratic movements intrigue a young grass-snake, the sun glinting on its green enamel skin. Everywhere new life has begun; even skywards, the freshening sou'westerly chases the big white clouds, revealing an occasional patch of radiant sunshine, as though eager to give us clear skies. Today I await a colleague who is going to assist me in stocking the lake; recent catches have been heavy, and it is important to keep a good head of fish in the waters.

I must relate one incident. Every year a married couple came to fish the reservoir from a neighbouring county: the father with his three sons aged five, seven and nine years, and mother – oh patient mother – sitting in the family car knitting and reading, awaiting the call to supply refreshments to the anglers. This year, for the first time, the five-year-old was being allowed to fish for trout. All three were fishing from the causeway which spans the water, mainly because it is easier for backcasting, being free from herbage that could be hooked. The father and even the two other lads were all confusing the five-year-old with impatient fervour.

After two hours none of them had made. I joined them to inspect permits and renew friendships, and daddy questioned the stocking rate of the waters – nothing new. Although I assured him that there were plenty of trout, he raised one eyebrow in silent disbelief. I recommended a certain lure and he pooh-poohed the suggestion, but in order to appear grateful he grudgingly condescended to use it with the five-year-old. Yes, you have guessed it – I can promise this is a true story! The five-year-old caught a rainbow trout weighing six pounds four ounces, which was duly landed by his father!

My companion and I set sail for the huge fish-cages which were moored in the middle of the lake; several hundred rainbows spent their time swimming non-stop around these confined, netted prisons. The catwalks of the cages were marked with cormorant droppings, and even the wily heron had attempted to penetrate the covered nets, sometimes successfully. Cormorants play havoc with the vulnerable stocks, which costs the authority a great deal of money. Of course, these predators are protected by law – these black satanic creatures who inflict such appalling damage on trout. Although I am an animal lover and a conservationist, I get cross at the wanton destruction of fish.

The stocking boat which we were towing was now straining at the sides with superb trout eager to escape into the wide expanse of water and, of course, a ninety per cent certain death. I'm afraid it doesn't do for one to get involved with the wildlife, but I must confess the older I become the more pacificatory I get.

June arrived in all its splendour, simply idyllic with warm temperatures, sunshine and gentle southerlies. The early morning haze was slowly clearing the valley, the air perfumed with heather from the moor. Two of us were to patrol the river from the little village bridge to the moor; the going would be rough, as at one stage the green, cultivated fields gave way to heather and scrub-covered moorland. The track is littered with granite rocks, invariably masked with lichens and spongy moss, making them slippery and dangerous. One stretch contains deep holding pools where poachers net the fertile waters; here we would have to exercise extreme caution and total awareness – it was going to be our area of surveillance.

The town hall clock struck seven as we put the car in the park. Shopkeepers were beginning to stir, some with buckets and brushes clearing yesterday's debris from the neat shop-fronts; cheeky paper-boys, their outsize bags slung awkwardly over their frail shoulders, made their happy way to print-scented shops where the proprietors, with pencils poised, marked the crisp new journals.

We crossed the stone bridge, dated 1647, where the steady flow swirls and eddies around the sturdy piers. My partner pointed out a sea-trout, motionless, its head to the current, only the occasional flick of its tail betraying its presence as it kept stationary against the flow. Soon we were walking the bank dressed in a diversity of colourful wild flowers, families of coots and moorhens exploring the underweed. Massive gnarled oaks are spaced along the riverside, their huge cavernous boles providing sanctuary for the resting salmon.

In the warmth of the sun, a recent hatch of midge bounced in black smudges over the eddies, tempting a brown trout whose rings widened to the bank. We saw a sight of indescribable beauty: a shaft of pale sunlight filtered through the willows on to a bulrush, where a dragonfly nymph clung in metamorphosis; already a swarm of vivid blue, pencil-like damselflies danced in capricious company, awaiting the arrival of their bigger cousin. The going was becoming slower and we found it necessary to make little detours around fallen trees and the ever-present granite. This seemed a good moment to rest and have a hot drink, which we shared in the company of a lone robin.

Kingfishers flashed up and down the flow, sometimes dropping like a stone, then reappearing moments later with a small, struggling fish. Their exquisite colours enhanced the riverside scene, while the ubiquitous dipper birds bowed to the water from the washed boulders. We continued on our way, the pine-covered slopes now visible through a break in the hillside; soon we would be nearing the danger area. Our conversation became muted as we scrambled laboriously over the rough, unfriendly rocks.

At last we arrived on the side of a rock-strewn hillside where we had cover and a superb view of the pool. The warmth of the rocks seeped through our clothing, producing the same effect as a hot bath; we lay fully stretched out, looking up at the clearing sky where a pair of regal buzzards circled in the blue vastness.

Our instructions were to remain and observe until six that evening when we would be relieved by two other bailiffs. Information had been laid that this particular pool was going to be netted within the next twenty-four hours. After a couple of hours resting on the warm rocks we were becoming sleepy; after lunch we were reluctant to make conversation. Both of us just lazed – apart from an occasional look through the glasses, each had his own private thoughts and in no way did we consider intruding on each other's.

By the foot of an old bog-oak, a water vole appeared; through my glasses I watched it wash its face, using its tiny feet with such fastidious care, framed in a backcloth of red campion. If I were a painter, what a superb study it would make – alas, I cannot even draw a loaf of bread. My chum was now breathing heavily, looking completely relaxed, and I had no desire to disturb him. A pair of playful otters had appeared, their antics so childlike as they chased each other in and around the dense waterside vegetation.

My mind immediately turned to Henry Williamson's *Tarka the Otter*, and I could understand absolutely why that great writer became captivated by them. The dark, sinuous coil of an eel was tossed into the air, where it was caught and dragged into the depths of the moving water. I nudged my colleague to witness this delightful scene, but he merely grunted and asked the time.

Four o'clock and the sun was shining fiercely. I was thirsty and reached for my flask: I stopped mid-way. Three men had arrived at the pool, apparently from nowhere, and my friend had spotted them as well. He muttered partly to himself and partly to me: 'Good God! You're not going to believe this – look!'

I studied the three, who were now preparing to secure a

net across the river. They say 'truth is stranger than fiction', and in this instance it was undeniable. Once again we had encountered our African poachers, and what's more, I was to learn later the author of the threatening letter.

After much difficulty and changing of position, I managed to contact the head bailiff by radio, who agreed to send more men to assist. Unfortunately, we had no idea where the poachers' vehicle was, as the spot was well away from any road or track. All we could do was wait and observe after the net was in place. I was surprised at the complete self-assurance and ease with which the men worked, showing little concern for any cover. It took them ten minutes to secure the net, about twenty feet across. One man simply swam to the other side, securing the net to the oak where the vole had performed its ablutions.

Now they had vanished – where? Our position on the hillside was roughly a hundred feet away from the net, and we dared not show ourselves in case they had retired into the scrub to wait until the net had produced a harvest – hopefully of salmon. Our eyes never left the net; a couple of times we thought we saw movement, which turned out to be rabbits. I wondered about the otters and the net, praying they wouldn't become entangled. The time dragged; it was now some two hours since we had reported the activity and the radio remained silent. Surely someone must call soon.

At precisely five-thirty the muted tones of the radio shocked me with the message: 'I can see you two clots as plain as anything – get your bloody fat bodies down. Zero out!' The vitriolic tones of the head bailiff informed us that the area was now covered and radio silence was to be observed. Periodical checks at the net through the glasses revealed moments conducive to fish having been gilled – or was it an otter? My companion dismissed my fears with the arrogant superiority of field knowledge, with a curt 'Impossible!' I hoped he was correct.

The sun was beginning to sink over the hill; I was cold and wanted to have a stretch, but feared the wrath of the ever-watchful HB. I needn't have bothered, for a quiet message told us that somebody was coming. My heart began to thump – I swear it could be heard over the surge of the river.

Three figures began to haul in the net, and judging by their excited remarks they seemed pleased with the catch. When the order was given to break cover I fell headlong down the rocks for no apparent reason – most odd – causing a nasty, deep gash on my face and head. However, I continued down towards the net, where already four bailiffs had apprehended the men. By now I was bleeding badly, which caused the head bailiff some concern.

The total haul was three fair-sized sea-trout and four salmon which, when sold, would certainly have compensated for the previous fines. However, I cannot help thinking that in a roundabout way he managed to get his measure of English blood – don't you? Or was it the result of African voodoo?

19

Striker

I had kept in touch with a pal since I left Australia many years ago. We had both been young boundary riders on a sheep station on the outskirts of Brisbane, and many a lonely night we had lain under the stars after a hard day's ride sharing our tucker – and many a Fosters we had consumed during our rare visits into town. Now, for the first time in thirty years, he was coming to England.

Naturally, I was looking forward to the meeting. The eighth of July was one of the rare days that we get in this country that was really hot, and the temperature had broken all records. I was pleased – it would at least be like old times for him.

'Snowy' Baker was a six-footer, heavily built, a superb rider and tough. His sense of humour was excellent and he was a good man to have behind you in trouble. He had seen service in Burma and had come through the war without a scratch. As I waited for the plane to arrive, I wondered if he had changed very much.

Eagerly searching the faces of the arrivals clearing customs, I saw Snowy accompanied by a slight, dark-skinned Aborigine clutching an ancient suitcase. The reunion was warm, and that night after dinner, over drinks, we talked well into the night. Snowy was manager of a large spread and several thousand head of woollies in central Queensland. As a well-deserved treat he had brought his number one man 'Striker' with him to show him the old country.

We said goodnight in the small hours and I left his hotel to make my somewhat hazy way home – the next couple of weeks were, I could see, going to tax my constitution. After that first evening together, I felt as though I had never left the bush.

139

Snowy was here to buy stock, and he looked forward to some fly fishing with me at the lakes. I had arranged to fix them both up with rods and tackle and to show them the excellent fishery of Fernworthy on Dartmoor.

The day began with clear skies and a burning sun with just a suspicion of wind – not conducive to good fishing, but it was warm and we had a lot of news to catch up on. I arrived outside the hotel at ten sharp, and already they were waiting, Snowy dressed in bush-jacket and shorts while Striker was in old grey flannels, off-white plimsolls and a highly coloured shirt. On his face he wore a big grin, waiting as he put it 'to tickle them 'um big rainybows with little fly'.

We chose a bankside where I knew it was possible to catch trout. I must confess that I have never seen anyone so awkward as Striker with a split-cane rod in his hand; how he managed not to hook all and sundry I shall never know. I'm afraid he wasn't very successful, and he soon lost interest and sat down beside us while we fished. Snowy managed to catch a brace of brownies and I never had a touch, but it was a pleasant day out together, especially as we finished back at my house in good form.

Now, as a special treat, I arranged fishing at the brand-new fishery called Wimbleball. An old shipmate of mine, Brian, was the bailiff and had agreed to coach Striker. Over lunch-time drinks we tied up the loose ends.

Monday was perfect – the sun with cloud and a pleasant breeze – as we journeyed to the border of Devon and Somerset. Rounding the bend after an uphill climb, we saw below us a long and inviting stretch of bejewelled water and grassy banks.

Introductions over, Brian led us to a spot where we would have privacy and, hopefully, good fishing. It wasn't long before we were into some good fish, but alas, Striker just could not get the hang of it at all. Brian departed after an hour to attend to his duties, leaving his pupil to fend for himself, and although Striker tried hard it was evident that his interest had gone. Thirty minutes decided that and, turning to Snowy, he announced, 'Boss, I'm going walkabout,' and with a brief wave of his bony arm he loped away along the water's edge.

The fishing was as fruitful as promised, and between us we landed three rainbows and a tiger trout all in perfect condition. From the net suspended in the water we selected a couple of beers that had been cooling and sat on the bank to enjoy our drink. Steaming towards us in the patrol boat were Brian and Striker. As they came alongside I saw that Brian was annoyed, and Striker had that hang-dog look that the Aborigines seemed to manage so well.

Brian accepted a lager and our dark friend took his drink and sat a little way off. Apparently, the bailiff had been called to a remote area of the fishery, where he had been

told he would find a poacher with ten rainbows on the bank
– the limit was five. Steaming up the narrow channel, he saw
Striker diving into the water and then emerging with a fish in
his mouth, his lean, brown body glistening in the hot sun.

'When I confronted him,' said Brian, 'he simply said "Fly
no good – Striker him catch rainybows with hands – him
good fella." '

Well, 'rules is rules'.

At the airport I said my goodbyes. Striker, with a twinkle
in his brown eyes, looked deeply into mine and said, 'No
flies on me, boss – eh?'

20

Visitors

Overnight there had been a sharp November frost; the lake was still, cloaked in a low, swirling mist that rolled along the surface of the water, uncertain whether or not to settle. It was the first frost of the winter on Dartmoor. I had arrived to inspect the fish-cages anchored in the middle of the fifty-four acre reservoir, and the dull red of the sun caught the frost-encrusted nets, transforming them into jewelled splendour. The lake was a thousand feet above sea level on the eastern granite ledge of the moor.

The lock of the mooring was frozen, which meant fiddling around with a box of matches to thaw the reluctant spring. With cold and painful fingers, I managed to release the chains to pull my boat to the shore. The activity brought to the bank the Canada geese who, understandably, sought human company in this lonely spot, as well as the titbits I always carried for them. When one is out alone in the wide expanse of Dartmoor I find it is quite natural to relate personally to the wildlife, and it's a wonderfully exhilarating feeling.

Entering the middle of the waters, a freshening south-westerly teased the mist, sending spumes off towards the pine-covered hills that flanked the water. The sound of my engine, although not too loud, was sufficient to panic a hundred sheldrake into the air, along with a company of greedy cormorants who were drying their wings on the catwalk of the cages. A long-legged heron wasn't too pleased either at my presence in the bay, but the rabbits ignored me as they continued nibbling at the rime-covered leaves of the dandelion.

I sailed towards the far end of the lake where the small

143

feeder-stream comes in and several mallards rose as one at my approach, disappearing over the larch cover. Making fast alongside the causeway, I walked the edge of the stream that barely moved; several trout were ready to reach the gravel beds to begin the spawning. The mossy bank was covered with the droppings of heron, confirming their prowess as superb fishers. It was deathly still, just the occasional flapping of a wood-pigeon from the woods disturbing the hush. I felt I was being watched by many eyes as I made for my craft.

By now the mist had gone, only isolated pockets remaining caught up in the branches of the pines, and the warmth of the sun on my face was pleasant as I steered for the cages on my return trip. The catwalk was covered in a sickly mass of yellow deposits from the many cormorants that had forsaken the estuaries for the easier pickings of the inland waters. My first task was to scrub them clean, which I did with vigour to get my circulation going. Shorewards, my eyes caught a car drawing to a stop alongside the bay. Four men got out and walked to the rails. The fishing season had been finished for some weeks, and it was unusual to see visitors at this remote spot and so early in the day.

The chore finished, I made thankfully for the mooring. I was chilled, regardless of the exercise, and looked forward to a hot drink. The geese had been attracted to the men, for they were making their way over to the tiny bay which tucked in beside the road. I was now out of sight of the men as I rounded the bend leading to the mooring, where I secured. My next duty was to inspect a reservoir some fifteen miles away, five hundred feet higher on the moor and no doubt much colder.

Suitably refreshed, I turned the car and travelled along the road in the direction of the visitors. The sound of my vehicle caused the men to turn from the water, watching my approach. I stopped behind their car, automatically noting the registration number. Greeting the four with a typically British remark about the weather, I saw that all of them were shivering and were most unsuitably dressed for this part of the country. They had the city dweller's pallor; two were in their forties, mean and hard and inclined to be offhand,

144

while the other two were quite ordinary, the kind of person you would find walking down any high street. They were at least more friendly, speaking in a southern accent; in fact, all of them were from London. I did comment on their dress advising them that Dartmoor could become quite savage at this time of the year, and suggesting warmer clothing.

Now it was their turn to question me. Did I know what that chap was doing out in the middle of the water. What was the platform out there? They obviously did not connect me with being the person they had seen. I played along, telling them it was the water bailiff inspecting the waters, and that the platform was a kind of testing station for water quality. I was not going to divulge the true nature of the structure after all – they could have been potential poachers. Anyway, they looked a bit suspect to me.

I learned that the four of them had decided – as they put it – to get away from their respective wives for the weekend to walk the moor, and they assured me that they had suitable gear stowed away in the boot of the car. I fetched a large flask of coffee from my car and offered them some. Taking turns at using the one cup, they became more talkative, plying me with questions. Could I recommend some good walks? Where was the best pub? Where was the Fernworthy forest? I answered the questions in turn, telling them that I, too, was on my way to Fernworthy.

We arranged to meet at noon at the local hostelry near Fernworthy, and I left them at the lakes talking among themselves. They told me that they had travelled through the night from London and had intended to have a snooze before meeting me.

The steady climb to the moor was a sheer delight in the now bright sunshine, passing cattle standing in silent circles, chewing with running noses, basking in the sun, their matted coats steaming. Moorland ponies huddled in the lee of a granite wall, some gently biting one another's necks in a kind of ritual. The scattered piles of dung were still covered in rime, partly thawing as the sun shone on the knobbly mounds. What grass there was offered little to the animals – it was cropped as tight as a young lover's chin. Only the woolly-clothed sheep seemed to enjoy the dwarf stems

145

regardless of the cold and my presence, barely moving as I passed close to them.

I could now see the water sparkling through the larch; the fish-cages were lined with cormorants digesting their meal of rainbow trout. As I reached the mooring, which was along-side an ancient hut circle, a cock pheasant, whose brilliant colours contrasted vividly with the grey of the granite, rose with exquisite beauty in the morning sunlight.

As the engine roared into life the cormorants immediately took off, settling randomly on the surface, some diving into the bitterly cold water. My bow wave sent the water crackling into long furrows towards the shore and the tall reeds where next year's dragonflies would climb and hatch. The frequent bleatings of the sheep were the only sounds that disturbed the serenity of the Dartmoor morning.

I reached the end of the lake, where the shore was dotted with the decayed, blackened stumps of trees and derelict buildings. It was the site of the old farm which had been flooded to make way for the reservoir. Stopping the engine, I mused a while, trying to imagine the homely scenes that had taken place here years ago, little children playing in the shade of the trees that were now rotting stumps, washed by the peaty moorland water. I almost thought I heard the farmer calling to his wife, 'Is dinner ready, maid?' How the senses could be fooled in this evocative setting – the magic of Dartmoor!

I shuddered as I started back to the mooring; alas, my flask was empty. It was a little past noon when I entered the low-beamed hotel bar; isolated groups of locals sat contemplating their pots of ale, while standing at the bar robust, ruddy-cheeked farmers carried on their good-natured banter in a haze of blue tobacco smoke. The publican automatically offered a greeting with 'What'll it be?'

I settled for a scotch and sat beside the wide, open fireplace that, alas, boasted an imitation log-effect electric fire; what sparse heat it produced promptly vanished up the dark, cavernous chimney. From an adjoining bar, a steady mechanical thud spewed from the sort of garish gambling machine that now seems to invade most pubs.

I rose to see if my expected guests had gone to the other

bar but, as I suspected, it contained a handful of young folk who were enjoying themselves. By twelve-forty there was still no sign of the four men; I decided to wait until one o'clock before leaving for home and lunch.

The thirteen-mile drive home along the narrow roads gave me time to speculate as to why the visitors had not turned up at the inn; the directions were literally foolproof, as a single road from the previous reservoir led almost to the venue. I was puzzled, and finally decided that they must have overslept.

A good lunch fortified me for the afternoon patrol of the

river. By three o'clock the sun had vanished behind a thick covering of low grey cloud, and it was becoming quite cold as I began to walk along the rough track. The patrol lasted until dusk without incident. Already owls were calling, but I still had time to have a last look around the reservoir where I had met the visitors during the early morning. It was only a matter of some four miles, which meant I would have just enough light to see before darkness fell.

The waters of the lake looked sombre in the fading light, and barely a ripple disturbed the leaden expanse. Huge flocks of starlings passed overhead, homeward-bound for their roost in the city; a lame fox paused on the water's edge, sniffing the air with strained caution before melting into the cover of beech. All was strangely quiet. Satisfied all was in order, I turned around on the dam, driving slowly along the lane which skirted by dense woodlands on one side of the pastures and on the other. A flock of sheep huddled in the shelter of the hawthorns, staring in silence as I passed.

By now the moon had broken through, casting a sheen over the trees and creating grotesque shapes in the woods. My eyes caught a glint in the cover as I passed – it was so sudden and quick that I was nearly convinced it was a trick of the moonlight, yet it nagged as I drove on. I had travelled at least a quarter of a mile before I felt compelled to return and satisfy my curiosity. Finding a gate in a nearby field, I reversed the car, driving slowly back, my eyes glued to the forest. Stopping a few yards away from the spot where I thought it had been, I walked the rest.

There was no mistaking it this time: it was the vehicle that I had seen earlier that morning carrying the men. It was now empty and partially covered with spruce branches; the giveaway was the reflection of the moon on a wing mirror that had first alerted me. The car had been driven into a row of young trees and an attempt had been made to camouflage it – I wondered why! A search of the area revealed nothing and, as it was now dark, I decided it would be prudent to wait until daybreak before doing anything further. However, I was unhappy and suspicious, and determined to contact the head bailiff on my return home.

A hot cup of tea was thrust into my hand as I settled down

for a chat with my colleague. I explained to him the events of the day and my suspicions, and he assured me that at first light members of the British Deer Society were going to carry out a cull in the area and that he would be present. In the meantime, I should go to Fernworthy next morning to collect some gear and then return to the lake, where we would meet up.

Overnight rain had moved into the south-west, and by eight o'clock a little drizzle was falling. My trip to Fernworthy was soon completed and I was eager to return to the lake to find out what was happening. The drizzle had stopped and I waited in the lane to allow a herd of Friesians to pass on their way to be milked; their huge, swollen udders swung in unison between mud- and dung-splashed legs while their doleful, film star eyes gave me sorrowful looks.

Outside my office stood a police car and other vehicles, but there was no sign of the occupants. The geese had gathered and were waiting expectantly on the bank and I felt rather guilty at having nothing to give them, for in my hurry to get away I had left the parcel of wholemeal my wife had put out for me. I promised them that I would return later, and felt rather silly, as I'm sure the two policemen and the head bailiff had heard me, for they had arrived and were looking down at me on the bank.

Introductions over, I was questioned at length by the police about the past day's events, and subsequently informed of the recent incident. Four members of the Deer Society had arrived at the woods at first light, and had split up in their search for the deer. They knew roughly where to expect them and carried radios to keep in touch. One of the stalkers had entered a small one-acre plantation of young beech when he stumbled across a recently constructed shelter of branches and spruce cover. It was, as he described it, a work of incredible skill and camouflage. Inside was a quantity of tinned food, shotgun and various items of clothing. He alerted his companion and the police, while the head bailiff kept a discreet watch on the area. The police informed us that the vehicle was of 'police' interest, the registration of the car having been given to them previously.

While I had been at Fernworthy the area had been staked

149

out, and the suspects were apprehended on their return just after eight o'clock, loaded with items of silver. They were now at the police station being 'seen to'.

After the stalkers had left, the police told the head bailiff and me that the four men were known house-breakers who specialised in burglaries of remote homesteads and large country houses. Their ploy was to camp out in nearby woods to avoid hotels and lodging houses, and then to drive straight on to the motorway and, within a matter of hours, be back in London.

Eventually the lakes settled down once more to serenity and peace. The head bailiff remarked, 'Do you know, I don't half fancy a cup of coffee – don't you?' I produced my flask, giving him the cup. I didn't tell him it was the one that had been used by the villains. Somehow I felt it would not have been right!

21
Midsummer Madness

Visitors had been arriving non-stop all the morning at the three lakes that sat on the eastern slopes of Dartmoor. By afternoon the fierce June sun was beating down on the shimmering waters, which echoed to the chatter and excited voices of tireless children. Parents lazed around; some were lying back soaking up the warmth, while others sat sedately in deck chairs reading, pretending not to notice the children taunting the geese that paddled in isolated groups waiting for titbits. An enterprising ice-cream vendor arrived in his multi-coloured van accompanied by a discordant rendering of the 'Stars and Stripes' which immediately brought the children running, shattering the comparative calm of the beauty spot.

This arrival was followed by a collection of acne-covered youths bedecked in crash helmets, their motorcycles creating a din like a swarm of killer bees. They parked their Hondas and began stripping off their 'uniforms' of chain-covered leathers, assorted scarves and jackboots. Their progress to the water's edge raised the heads of slumbering bodies, especially when one of the group switched on his radio and danced an impromptu jig to the rendering of a pop song. It became necessary for me as the bailiff to exercise my authority gently but firmly which, I am pleased to say, produced the desired result.

This was only one of many incidents that occurred during the day and, what with the heat of the sun, I felt a need to disappear for an hour to refresh myself. A thousand acres of pine forest surround the waters, and in the middle of the plantation is the Quakers' burial ground. A colony of these fine people lived and worked the fertile land for five hundred years in an atmosphere of utter tranquillity and beauty, eventually leaving for the Americas, and their forebears sleep beneath the shade of tall larch and wild honeysuckle, only the song of birds disturbing the silence of their graves.

I made straight for this peaceful area, leaving behind the hordes of holidaymakers who were all intent on enjoying this glorious Sunday. A narrow grass track led me into the heart of the woods, bringing instant relief from the sun – the tall trees let in very little light. Here the honeysuckle gave off its heady, sweet scent and squirrels darted between the trees, annoyed by my presence. All was still as I went deeper into the forest.

Soon I came to the burial ground, a two-acre patch surrounded by a dry stone wall covered in ivy, bladderwort and pink campion. Near a rough wooden gate a granite post leaned lop-sidedly, bearing a copper plaque, green with verdigris, announcing the resting place of the 'Friends'. A solitary wood-pigeon preened its feathers on the gate. I rested on a nearby fallen larch, breathing deeply the pungent scent of the earth and wondering about the forgotten band of happy people who lived here all those years ago.

A faint smell of wood smoke awakened me from the reverie. This was disturbing, as I knew the nearest residence was at least two miles away and fire in these woodlands was a very serious threat indeed. I followed a track that ran parallel to the graveyard to where a cluster of derelict buildings that were purported to have been used by the Quakers nestled in a small copse of hazel trees. Here the smell of smoke became stronger.

From the trees came the figure of a man, tall and stooped, carrying a bundle of dead branches. It was his dress that puzzled me – he was clothed in the garb of a long-ago peasant, and a vacant expression on his face showed not the slightest interest in me. I asked him if he had lit a fire, as no unauthorised person was allowed in this area and lighting a fire was in no way permitted. Silently he beckoned me to follow him.

I thought I had perhaps stumbled upon a tramp living among the shells of the outbuildings, and I was determined to make him douse the fire. He walked on ahead completely unconcerned, shifting his load from side to side to ease his arms. By now I could see a spiral of smoke rising from the buildings and at once became alarmed.

Rounding the bend, we followed a path which led to the buildings; a babble of voices told me that it was more than likely a group of 'hippies' who had moved in. This I imagined must have happened in the last two weeks, as I had recently had a conversation with the forestry manager regarding the extreme fire hazard that had arisen due to the long dry spell. The sight that greeted me stunned me.

In a small courtyard, flanked on three sides by the old buildings, stood a long, wooden table where at least thirty people – men of all ages, women and children – were seated. Two lurcher-type dogs were eating the scraps of meat that were being tossed from the table. Everyone was dressed in the Quaker fashion and their conversation was punctuated with 'thees' and 'thous', the language of long ago. A large, controlled fire was burning at the end of the yard, where my visitor had promptly dumped his bundle of wood. This was obviously a convention of the 'Society of Friends' who were enacting some kind of ritual dinner. But why wasn't I informed about this? I was annoyed, partly because my hour's rest had been rudely disturbed. I left at once for the lakes and my vehicle – nobody had taken the slightest notice of my enquiries.

Once again I was back in the present-day world of noisy ice-cream vendors, transistors and the general hubbub of the holidaymakers. I quickly left for the manager's house, which was three miles away, hoping he would be at home. Silently, I was seething.

John was having tea with his family on the lawn overlooking the main lake, enjoying his day of rest. My arrival was greeted with an invitation to tea, which in normal circumstances would have been very welcome. I blurted out my discovery, which was met with surprise and then annoyance; with profound apologies on having disturbed his day, I offered to drive him to the offending area, which he readily accepted. Our progress was hampered by the many cars that thronged the narrow lanes which traversed the lakes. John was becoming agitated, partly by our slow, laboured process, but mainly at the thought of what might happen if his beloved forest caught fire. It would be disastrous. Why hadn't he been informed? We made our slow way to the burial ground, giving vent to our feelings.

Leaving the car at the entrance to the lane, we ran all the way to the buildings, arriving breathless at the site. The courtyard was deserted! The overgrown buildings stood silent; only an old barn-owl sat eyeing us from the ancient hayloft, mocking us. I was speechless! The look of annoyance darkened my companion's face; turning to me, he snapped, 'What's this then – some kind of joke?' I was dumbfounded, but managed to voice a lame explanation.

From the corner of one of the old mangers I pointed to the dying embers of the fire. He was puzzled as we scraped earth over the ashes. Turning to me, he said quietly 'Perhaps you need a rest.'

I knew I had had a hectic time lately – but I also knew what I saw. And what about the fire?

22

A Remembrance

He came towards me with the crab-like gait of extreme old age, every step he took apparently requiring immense effort as first the left leg moved, purely as a reflex action, followed by the dragging right. A pair of watery, hooded eyes blinked in the morning sunshine, his aquiline features carrying a permanent look of bewilderment – or was it a slightly disdainful view of modern life?

In a voice charged with emotion, he enquired if I happened to be the bailiff; the thin treble tones trailed off before he had finished the question. He stood bent, his head leaning to one side as he waited patiently for my reply. The faded tweed jacket hung limply from spare shoulders, reminding me of Shakespeare's 'sans teeth – sans everything!' I invited this ghost of a man to sit on the one and only one spare chair, but the plain, wooden seat offered little comfort to his weary bones. Nodding a thank you, he slowly settled on the creaking elm with a relieved sigh. As he rubbed his tired leg I saw that his hands were misshapen, the huge bulbous knuckles projecting like organ-stops from the blue-veined parchment of his skin. I waited for him to speak as he drew in gasps of breath, producing little whistles from loosely fitting dentures.

Outside the tiny granite office which tucked neatly into the rocky hillside, the September sun bathed the waters of the lake in sparkling warmth. A pair of inquisitive geese waddled from the bank to the doorway as if to witness this man from the past. With faltering speech he related his story of many years ago when he had first fished the lakes as a young boy. He told of the carefree days of his youth and his love for these tranquil waters that sit in the shade of the

156

Dartmoor hills, and I became fascinated as the tale unfolded the distant past.

'I wanted to pay a last visit before I die and see my plot where I shall be buried in the village churchyard, which lies in the valley not far from my beloved lake.'

General Chadwick – that is the name I shall give him – unfolded that morning an endearing story which I can now tell. His grave has been carpeted with the past three seasons' primroses – his favourite flowers.

'I always remember as a lad being brought to the lakes by my father who was a keen flyfisher,' the General began.

Sometimes I was permitted to accompany him on his fishing trips to Scotland for the salmon …' Raising a thin arm towards the water, his eyes seemed to be pulling memories from the air. 'Over there, in the bay, I cast my first fly. Never forget the Greenwell Glory. I felt a challenge as I thrashed the water which, alas, succeeded in frightening the fish away. Papa scolded me no end until I was able, after many hours, to land my fly softly. But I never hooked a trout that day. The brown trout, although small, made excellent sport; father and his friends stocked the waters after getting permission from the water board. It was operated as a private fishery, you know. Some of my school holidays were spent with friends here on the water; such delightful, exciting days they were.'

He stood up, rubbing his bottom and waving aside my offer of a folded jacket to act as a cushion; his eyes now sparkled as the memories came flooding through his tired brain. From his sagging pocket he took a packet of cigarettes, offering one to me. He seemed pleased at my acceptance, remarking, 'I'm glad that you, too, indulge in the "filthy habit" as they call it these days.'

I held the lighted match to his shaking cigarette and he sucked at the tiny flame like a boy taking his first illegal puffs. The small crested signet ring on his little finger looked unusually big against the shrunken folds of flesh as he inhaled the soothing nicotine. It appeared to refresh him; holding his back he slowly sat down, once more drifting back into his reverie.

'Oh yes, my word they were truly exciting days. I caught my first fish on my third visit. Papa was away at the time – in the army; I desperately wanted him to see my first trout. You know, I carried it home tied to the handlebars of my cycle and presented it to Mama with pride – as if it had been a twenty-pound salmon.'

He became silent as he finished his cigarette, gazing over the lake from the little window, reliving the long-ago adventures on the bankside. Without warning, he rambled off on another half-forgotten memory.

'Giles, my friend, was killed you know – in India, at the Khyber Pass. A great fisherman he turned out to be, although when we were in the army together he was inclined to be idle.' I expressed interest in his career with the British army, gently encouraging him to relate his adventures.

'Were you ever in the army?' he asked, assuming the authoritative tone of a man used to command.

'No sir,' I replied respectfully, 'but I did serve with the Royal Navy during the war,' adding slyly, 'the senior service, sir.' He chuckled at my veiled insolence.

'Well now Commodore,' he retorted gleefully, automatically promoting me to exalted rank, 'what ships did you serve in – my brother was in command of a destroyer you know.'

For the next fifteen minutes or so he took me with him on patrol through the troubled, notorious pass where many Englishmen had made history picking up awards for bravery. Not once did he mention his rank or, come to that, the awards he had won; it was only later that I learned of his superb antecedents – an extremely brave and talented officer, one of those who were the backbone of the late British Empire. Such men are rare.

It was now an hour since we had first met and I could see he was becoming tired. He rose awkwardly from the hard chair; offering his hand, he said, 'Thank you, "Commodore", for listening to an old man – I do hope we meet again. Keep up the good work.' As he made slowly for the door he half turned, giving me a salute. I returned it in a true naval fashion and felt sad as I watched him walking to his car. I never saw him again.

For the rest of the day I felt strangely unhappy; the meeting with the old warrior had greatly affected my mood. What it had also done, however, was enhance my imagination as I patrolled the lake, visualising the scenes that had taken place all those years ago.

Two weeks after that memorable meeting I was in conversation with an elderly angler whom I had often seen on the waters but had never really had much to do with. He also was a retired army officer of high rank.

'I say, bailiff – the old gentleman I saw leaving your office a couple of weeks ago, do you recall? Would that have been General Chadwick DSO and two bars?'

I replied that certainly the gentleman was a retired officer.

159

'He served in India, but I cannot tell you his name. I only hope it was.'

'I'm damned sure that was old Chaddy, I was too late to reach him before he drove off; I vaguely recognised him from where I was fishing just across the bank. We met last year at our reunion. What a pity – a great man, stubborn as a bloody mule and my God, how he loved a scrap!'

I remained silent, hoping he would tell me more about my interesting visitor. I made no move to walk away, and he seemed to sense my reluctance to leave; he began to fill his pipe and, between puffs of the freshly lit briar, he looked under his eyes at me, eventually burning his fingers on the dying match.

'Damn!' He half addressed me and the water. 'Yes – Chaddy was quite a card. The men worshipped him, followed him everywhere; loved his fishing too. Did you know he fished the lake as a lad?'

'Yes, I did know sir, he began to tell me about his early life but unfortunately he became tired. I should have liked to have heard more. I found him an interesting man indeed,' I answered.

'Well now, there were three of us, all eager to fish: Chaddy, Nigel and myself . . .'

I interrupted, telling him that Nigel had been killed.

'Yes, yes – what else did he tell you, eh?' he asked in a tone bordering on a rebuke.

'Well sir, not very much,' I replied. 'As I've said, he became tired before he had finished relating his boyhood.'

'Mm – yes, well, as I was saying ...' I detected a mild reprimand for the interruption as he continued. 'The three of us spent many a happy time here, especially in Clampitt Bay. Some damn good fish in that water. It was Chaddy who first caught a trout – the artful blighter. Nigel first saw him, he was some distance away; I was just around the bend fishing, never forget, I was so damn jealous of him as I really believed I was the better fisherman. Chaddy had first seen the brownie rising, taking something or another; as Nigel and myself hadn't had a take, let alone seen a fish, we decided to fish further along the bank. As I say, Nigel – so he told me – kept looking to see if he would manage to hook it; I was out of sight, praying I would be the first to capture a fish. However, quite some time later, Nigel calls out to me: "He's got one!" Sure enough, I returned to Nigel so that I could see the catch. It was only a small one, but he had caught it. Nigel, who later became a superb angler, complained that he had seen Chaddy bring the fish to the shallows, only to lose it as it wriggled off the hook. Chaddy jumped into the water with his net and managed to scoop it up. Damned unsporting we thought, but Chaddy, as I've mentioned, was damn stubborn, determined to have it come what may. I suppose it was the determination that earned him his well-deserved decorations. He captured an enemy gun position that had been plaguing us for days, you know.

'Well, this will not catch my supper, bailiff. Nice talking to you – goodbye.' The conversation ended abruptly and I was dismissed, continuing my patrol.

For the next few weeks as I walked the reservoir I would spend some time sitting on the bank in Clampitt, imagining those boys of long ago who eventually went away to make history and one, of course, to die. There is a tiny stream that trickles off the hillside into the lake – it's a lonely spot, and the plantations of pine, oak and birch come down to the water's edge. The area abounds with a diversity of wildlife, and it is also a favourite haunt of the heron. Not far away, just into the woodlands, was the area where the community of Quakers lived for five hundred years having been forced, as it were, into the wilderness before it became a reservoir – by the then Bishop of Exeter. The atmosphere is steeped in a million memories, now added to by the tales of the old warriors. I sit in the soft, mellow sunlight sometimes and dream of those far-off days. Early morning is best, when I have only the birds and the sighing wind blowing through the trees for company. Sometimes an arrogant wild mink will explore within a few feet of me, or a harmless grass-snake might take a morning swim. It is a wonderful spot to heal a troubled mind. Try it next time you are in the Dartmoor area.

A few years ago I learned with sadness of the death of the General; it was as if I had known him for a long time instead of only hours – such is the power of memories. I have visited his grave in the tiny churchyard where the moorland breeze gently caresses the primrose-studded mound, and I am reminded of the tremendous history and heritage of this island of ours, that has shown the world what a proud thing it is to be called an Englishman.

23

Scouse

I think it would be fair to say that I have never seen a father and son look so much alike. They arrived at the lakes just before noon. The father slid carelessly from the driving seat of an old Ford, whose bodywork bore scars of past encounters with other vehicles. The rear window was practically obliterated by coloured stickers, proclaiming all of the visits to the various seaside resorts not forgetting, of course, that the lions had been seen at Longleat. From the windscreen, two enormous cowboy dolls swung with the momentum of the hastily stopped vehicle.

From the passenger side, an exact miniature replica of the driver emerged from the cracked leather seat like a moth from a chrysalis, arrogantly chewing gum while at the same time wiping a dripping nostril with the palm of his grubby hand. I met them at the entrance to the permit office.

'Howdy!' The pseudo-western greeting came from the short, spare, middle-aged man whose deeply lined, ferret face framed a ridiculous hair style that was more in keeping with a female – the deep fringe and long hair to each side of his head flopped every time he spoke. Two restless brown eyes were constantly on the move as I explained the fishing, while he fingered a large gold-coloured medallion that hung at his throat, nestling in a bed of wiry ginger hairs. His entire presence was engulfed in an aromatic aftershave perfume that added to his bizarre appearance.

Looking up from the depths of his father's tight checked trousers, a boy of about ten busily picked at his nose, open-mouthed, listening intently to every word. He, too, sported the hair style, and his restless eyes were determined

163

not to miss a thing. A smaller version of his father's medallion hung at the pale, scraggy neck.

It was their first visit to the fishery although, as I was informed, 'We sure have fished all over the place.' This information was imparted from the corner of the man's mouth, obviously from force of habit, and was delivered in a nasal accent that reeked of the Mersey and mid-Atlantic. I was also told that his name was 'Wayne' – that accounted for the western greeting, I suppose – and that his son went under the colourful name of 'Trigger'.

As they both filled in the statutory permit and licence I checked to confirm if, indeed, these were their correct names; apparently they were. Mr Wayne O'Brien and Master Trigger O'Brien had just ridden in – pardon me, driven in – from Plymouth. The man insisted on shaking my hand after I had given him all the information; I noticed for the first time he wore several rings, one a large feminine cluster of diamonds that looked decidedly out of place on his bony fingers. Noticing my interest in the ostentatious trinket, he waved it in my face, remarking in an off-hand way, 'Picked it up in Rio.' He promptly left for his car, followed closely by Trigger, who by now was pulling at the worn wad of gum with grubby fingers.

I have seen many types of people in my work as a water bailiff, and am not easily surprised by some of the specimens that now roam this world. But I must say these two interested me – if I were a film producer I would definitely cast them as the 'artful dodgers'. The speaking out of the corner of the mouth convinced me that the man must have seen service, at some time or other, in HM establishments.

They settled for a spot on the far side of the bay where, in the shade of a big waterside birch, they made their temporary base. I watched them through my field-glasses and was appalled to see the youngster light up a cigarette with apparent expertise. The father did likewise. It occurred to me that the lad should by rights have been attending school, but more pressing duties then made me lose interest. Nevertheless, father and son had left their mark.

Towards sundown I made my final patrol around the lake, finding that many fish had been caught. My last visit was to

'Wayne' and 'Trigger'; by the look on their faces they seemed mighty pleased with life.

'Hi! Been great today – sure got nice fish in your waters. Yep, I reckon this is the gear!' He greeted me with exaggerated flamboyance.

'How many have you caught?' I enquired, eager to respond to his cheerfulness. Wayne called to his son.

'Trig! How many, pardner?' I thought the cowboy idiom was a trifle absurd, especially as it was spoken in all seriousness. The boy by now looked tired, but he held six fingers up for his father's inspection.

'Not bad, eh?' The man addressed the remark more to the air than to me. I noticed a little further off a pair of black waders lying forlorn on the bank, partly hidden behind some gorse. I told him as we do not permit wading this would save him the trouble of bringing them. My advice was dismissed airily with a wave in the direction of the boots.

'We always bring them with us – part of the scene, don't you think?' I couldn't be bothered to try to understand the logic of the remark.

They had one hour before closing in which to catch their permitted eight fish between them as I bade them goodbye, reminding them to fill in their return card. A brilliant full moon lit up the waters as the remaining anglers left the banks for home. Another successful day's fishing here in the south-west had come to a close.

The following Tuesday my colleague, who was responsible for waters high on the moor, was on leave, so apart from my normal duties it was necessary for me to visit his fisheries to make a licence check, and to feed the caged fish.

Such early mornings in June are a joy to behold; the big expanse of water glittered in the sunlight, and there were only the geese and wildlife for company. The silent pine plantations on the hills bathed in the soft warmth of the early morning sun were a picture of tranquillity and peace. In such surroundings one finds it hard to imagine the intense violence and unhappiness that is sweeping the world at every moment. And yet, as I thought those thoughts out here on Dartmoor, I had just witnessed the assassination of a young rabbit by a fiery stoat in the cover of a blaze of heather.

165

The drama took place in complete silence, witnessed by an exquisite dragonfly and a large grass-snake, who then slipped into the water. I suppose one must not look too deeply into the natural predation that has taken place since time began.

It was well past nine o'clock as I left for the higher reaches of the moor, and the twelve-mile journey through some of the finest and most dramatic countryside in England took less than half an hour.

Through the tall larch I could see that several anglers were already fishing, making the most of the morning rise. Prolific hatches of alder kept the trout busy, as the entire lake was peppered with feeding-rings. I made an unhurried patrol of the water, checking and yarning with the fishermen, some of whom were fishing from boats. Everyone I met enthused not only about the fishing, but also about the superb day and surroundings. It certainly was a delight.

After checking the boat rods it was time to take a look at the far end of the waters. Stopping my boat in a forest of tall reeds, I disturbed a host of blue damselflies who took flight, creating an enchanting cameo against the drab granite rocks where several adders basked in the sun. Just above the water's edge a colourful woodpecker rapped at an old elm, the staccato knocking echoing over the silent moor. I sat on the bows of my beached craft marvelling at the stamina of the little creatures, and wondered flippantly if at any time they experienced a headache.

Scrambling gingerly over the mass of small rocks, I reached the soft, spongy carpet of moss and heather and walked upstream to a knot of anglers spaced along the water's edge. Most had captured fish and, judging by the good-natured banter, all were happy and contented. I retraced my footsteps to the boat. The fish having gone off feed, the anglers were taking advantage of the lull to enjoy picnic lunches, while some just lazed in the warmth of the sun. Sailing downstream towards the dam, I saw two fishermen lurking in the lea of an ancient hut circle. Drawing nearer I experienced a wave of recognition: it was the Liverpudlian, with his son in tow. They both greeted me with warm affection as I joined them, squatting on a rock alongside.

166

'Fancy a beer, mate?' the father asked, pulling the top off a can of beer and sending a fine, beery spray over the boy's trousers.

'I won't, thank you – I'm just off for my lunch.'

'Please yourself, fella,' was the laconic reply. The boy was gorging himself on a large, creamy doughnut; the filling spread around his nose and mouth. As he attacked the pastry with savage vigour, I noticed a cigarette end wedged behind his little pink ear.

'No school today, young man?' I asked, more by way of making small talk than seeking information.

'Naaw!' He spat as he searched in a carrier bag for more goodies, promptly dismissing me. His father, sensing his unwitting rudeness, offered an explanation: "E don't like school, I guess he learns more from me than those dang fancy questions the teachers gives him. 'E likes fishing, more natural, like, for kids. That's right, Trig – ain't it?' Trigger looked up, a face full of jam and cream, and just grunted. I noticed once again the same pair of tired-looking waders lying a little way off in the shade of a bush. There was something odd about them, and an ill-fitting patch on the side of one boot curled in the sun.

'I see you've brought your waders again,' I remarked casually, which brought a knowing look from the lad to his dad.

'Yep!' was the crisp reply.

Good Lord, doesn't this man ever stop play acting? I thought. I suppose he now thinks he's Gary Cooper. The friendliness vanished in an instant and silence fell, signalling my departure. I could almost feel the sigh of relief they gave as I climbed aboard and sailed for the mooring on the opposite bank. Something wasn't quite right about these two, but I just couldn't put my finger on it.

The season progressed with a mixture of sun and rain, but on the whole the summer so far had been better than average. Anglers continued to visit the reservoirs and rivers, and I saw the two many times fishing the various waters – and on every occasion the waders were present but never worn. Eventually a chance remark from a holidaymaker solved the mystery.

The August Bank Holiday was blessed with clear skies and

sunshine, bringing many visitors into the county. It was a perfect holiday Monday with hordes of happy, inquisitive people thronging the lakes. Just before lunch I was called to the bankside by a young lad to investigate a dead animal floating in the water. The rails of the roadside fence were lined with onlookers, who no doubt considered this spectacle a pleasant diversion from just watching the anglers fishing. My every move was followed closely as I fished a rather plump wild mink from the water. On reaching the roadside, several people crowded around me to see the sad, floppy body, whose bared teeth drew gasps of 'Oh, how vicious' and the like.

I took the body to the back of my office for burial, followed by a rather intellectual old man. He watched me dig a hole and bury the carcass, smiling at me with friendly nods. It was plain that he wanted company, and possibly information. I knew the signs only too well; anyway, I enjoy the odd encounter with interesting folk and he certainly looked like one to me. He introduced himself as Doctor Evans, on holiday from Cardiff – where else? – a biologist who plied me with many questions about my work and the surrounding area.

I enjoyed the chat and was delighted to learn about many aspects of wildlife that I never knew, especially one observation he had made concerning a pair of fishermen that he had seen returning to their car after a day's fishing. He told me of a man and a boy who had come up from the lake after fishing.

'You see, I was interested as to the species of fish that they had caught. The man was most obliging, producing from his bag several fine rainbow trout which he offered for sale. I was delighted to purchase such fresh fish and bought five – I paid him six pounds, which I thought was well worth it. I didn't wish to appear greedy, but he quickly showed me five others inside the fishing bag.' I replied with unashamed pride that our fish were excellent. He continued: 'The angler, whom I thought was either American or possibly Canadian, went to his car to fetch a plastic bag for my fish when I noticed that some fish seemed to be oozing out from two rubber waders – most odd.'

I thanked him for our talk, and took my leave of him. Well, well, so that was their game – a perfect cover under which to smuggle fish from the reservoir. They would certainly be watched from now on. Strangely, for the next couple of weeks I saw no sign of the two cowboys.

Three weeks later to the day I had just stocked the lake with many hundreds of trout and was securing my boat to the moorings, when I was greeted with, 'Hi! How yer doing mate? Been stocking, I see – how many have you put in?' I looked up from padlocking the mooring chain and into two dark, flashing eyes. Wayne and Trigger had just hit town, complete with waders draped around the neck. The boy stood looking at me, blowing bubbles from a wad of pink gum that was wedged in the side of his mouth. I assured them that it would indeed be a rewarding day for them – and for me, I hoped.

They continued on their way along the bank; the boy appeared to be excited, as he looked up at his father talking rapidly. A sharp cuff on his head delivered by his 'pardner' cut short the conspiratorial excitement.

It was going to be a long day for me, as I intended to keep them under constant surveillance, aiming to stop the wholesale stealing of fish which no doubt had been an easy source of income for them. On the father's permit he was allowed to take five fish while the boy's limit was three -- all for a combined cost of six pounds. Selling the catch would make a healthy profit; needless to say, the gain on extra smuggled fish would be considerable. However, I must add quickly that these kind of 'fishmongers' happily are rare.

During the warm afternoon some fishermen returned to the office with their limit bags, thanking me for a good day. One kindly pensioner, especially, was very pleased with his catch, volunteering information that confirmed my previous talk with the doctor.

'Bailiff, you know some people are nothing but damn cheats. I went into the bushes for a pee and saw a small boy, whom I might add was smoking – couldn't have been more than ten or eleven – actually putting fish into waders. It was obvious he was up to no good.'

During the day I kept a discreet watch on the two as they

169

fished non-stop, noticing that they took their refreshments standing up while fishing. By five-thirty that evening they had caught twenty fish and I wondered when they were going to make a move. Two more rainbow later, they made tracks for their vehicle. I was looking forward to the confrontation with the two poachers – or should I say rustlers?

At a given signal another bailiff joined me to assist with the cheats. I joined them as they reached their car, both looking mighty pleased with themselves.

'Had a good day?' I asked, closing with them.

'Sure have mate,' cowboy Wayne replied, depositing his fishing bag in the boot; he seemed reluctant to unslip the waders from his neck, hoping no doubt I would go away. My companion and I walked on a little way, allowing him to place the waders in the back of the car. Turning back, I called out, 'Wayne – just a point.' I reached him as he nervously lit a cigarette. Opening the door of the car, I casually knocked on one of the boots saying, 'Why for goodness' sake do you saddle yourself with those cumbersome waders?' He recoiled from the gesture saying, 'Force of habit, I guess. Yep – force of habit.'

The other bailiff asked to inspect his bag. Wayne eagerly offered it for inspection, saying, 'Sure thing. Great fish – some fishery this, and well run.'

I slid one of the waders up, revealing the rainbows that oozed out until, from one boot alone, twelve trout lay exposed in slimy splendour. The boy just stood, still chewing, looking at his father, who by now was breaking wind copiously. Father and son looked a picture of dejection as we confiscated the entire catch and tackle, cautioned him, and warned him of possible prosecution under the Theft Act. He lamely denied that he had ever carried out this kind of deception before, regardless of the fact that we could produce witnesses. The amount of money he made over the period must have been considerable.

I know one sad fact: that father has spawned a potential future poacher, who no doubt considers it the normal practice to lie and cheat.

24

Scarback's Farewell

It had been at least six whole weeks since the county had
seen or felt any appreciable rainfall. Rivers were running
dangerously low; fishing had practically come to a standstill,
and what fish there were remained well and truly hidden.

'When is it going to rain?' was the phrase on everyone's
lips. All kinds of theories were being voiced. 'Perhaps the
greenhouse effect has started' or 'I'm sure Russia is to blame',
and so on. How and why, of course, was never explained. In
post office queues, shops, pubs and even in the 'House' the
weather was the number one topic.

Never did one enjoy ambiguous popularity as much as the
weatherman, on both radio and television; the whole country
would listen in hushed silence to the voice that would say
once again, 'A deep anti-cyclone still remains stationary over
the British Isles, temperatures above average, still no sign of
any rain.' And so it went on, day after day, until people
accepted the dry skies with resigned stoicism.

Reports from the estuaries alerted water bailiffs to the fact
that many salmon were gathering in the channel waiting for
the river to spate. The journey to the spawning beds was a
long and hazardous one, and it was essential for the rivers
to swell as a great deal of water was needed to ensure a
reasonably easy passage to the upper reaches.

Scarback was on her second visit to her birthplace high
on Dartmoor but, owing to the lack of water, she was
unable to leave the shelter of the huge oak whose massive,
cavernous roots on the river bank have provided sanctuary
for hundreds of years to the migratory fish. The gnarled trunk
leaned towards the ancient hump-back bridge where, since
a seedling, it had grown in company with the silent granite

mass, and now, over the years, its massive branches had come almost to embrace the lichen-covered arches in a kind of silent affection.

Scarback had entered the river over six weeks ago, managing to reach New Bridge, her familiar resting place. But the very next day the river level had fallen dramatically, making it impossible for her to continue her pilgrimage. She was becoming tense and agitated; her whole body felt strange. Although she had been resting as a virtual prisoner beneath the oak, with all her strength conserved, she felt tired and confused.

An irritation on her head caused her constantly to rub herself against the blackened roots, but even several minutes of twisting and turning brought her no relief. Two angry red sores had appeared on her head, about the size of tenpenny pieces; the constant rubbing had aggravated the lesions until they became tiny, deep craters, which were now becoming covered in a faint white bloom of fungus. The constant shaking of her head as she tried to dislodge the infection only made her more tired.

She was now five years plus, weighing a good eighteen pounds, with her belly simply bursting with thousands of tiny orange pearls that she was eager to deposit in her birth place. Her last visit had been so different; although fraught with danger, she had never felt this strange weariness.

A sharp flick of her tail sent her out of the hollow towards the surface; a big orange moon bathed the shallow water in a warm sheen. A freshening wind came in from the south-west bringing teased tufts of cloud, like huge kites, across the moonlit sky, which sailed unhindered away towards the wood-covered skyline.

Silhouetted against the night sky, an old dog-fox took his nightly drink, his paws spreading the soft sand of the foreshore into giant-sized pads as the river became lower every day.

Two shadowy forms passed on the opposite bank, stopping by the oak tree to whisper in furtive conspiracy. The elder of the two shook his head, urging his companion on; the fox pricked his ears momentarily and melted away into the undergrowth.

Scarback retreated once more into her watery cavern. All was quiet; the gentle flow of the river as it swirled and eddied around the granite piers sighed through the darkened hours.

Two young sea-trout that had been the salmon's constant escort settled once more above her – but not for long, for the salmon began once more the constant rubbing against the roots; her head ached. Disturbed by the fretful movement, the young trout moved a little way off into the shallows.

Through the moonlit surface film, Scarback could see the wavering outline of the heron standing motionless: it had spotted the trout. She settled and watched from below.

A sudden flash of broken light shattered the surface of the water as the bayonet thrust of the heron's beak impaled one of the fish, its mate swimming off for deeper water. Within seconds the surface of the water had become still once more, and Scarback could see the heron poised again to attack, but the surviving trout had edged much closer to the salmon, taking in gulps of water in its need for more oxygen.

During the long, silent hours of the night Scarback, in her semi-comatose state, relived her previous encounters along this run of the river, remembering that the next point would be at the weir where the noisy motorway runs alongside. It was there that she had nearly become snared. The discomfort she was now experiencing was similar to the time when she had had a loop of wire caught over her shoulders, although she had been able, after a time, to rub it off. But this time it was different, and no amount of rubbing seemed to ease the constant burning.

Dawn broke in a sunless sky, the wind almost at gale force, stripping the trees and sending a constant shower of yellowing leaves into the sluggish flow. As far as the eye could see, huge banks of black nimbus clouds heralded a likely storm. Even the birds became silent as they huddled in the nooks and crannies of the trees that were being stripped bare by the ferocity of the wind. Everyone seemed to be waiting in the foreboding atmosphere of this autumn morning.

A heavy clay-carrying lorry thundered over the bridge, sending a flock of pigeons from the arches into the air; its

driver called out to a farmer who was walking the tarmac
road, 'Looks like it's coming at last!', and rumbled off into
the distance.

The wind gave a terrific shriek and flashes of sheet
lightning lit up the sky, followed by tremendous claps of
thunder. A spotting of big raindrops pitted the water. The
pigeons had already returned to the arches, two moorhens
made for the shelter of the thick reeds and Scarback felt the
river being charged with oxygen as the water stirred. She
felt less tired, and became impatient to continue her passage
upriver.

By now the rain was falling heavily, accompanied by
intermittent thunder and lightning. In a nearby field the
cattle were revelling in the monsoon-like downpour, calling
out to one another in ecstasy at the luxurious soaking
of their dusty bodies. For the rest of the day it rained
non-stop and within three hours of the downpour the
river had risen to half spate, becoming coloured, full of
floating herbage and plastic rubbish as it scoured the banks
clean.

Scarback began once more her interrupted voyage upstream; the flow was strong, and she swam effortlessly under
the bridge and along the winding ribbon of peaty-coloured
water towards the weir and the next fish-pass. The rain
had eased slightly but the wind continued to tear at the
water, creating a boiling cauldron along the entire length of
the river.

The salmon surfaced every so often to view her surroundings, for the river was the colour of thick coffee; she kept
station mid-stream, making for the motorway bridge where
the traffic thundered almost non-stop.

Once under the bridge the river winds gently away from
the noise of the traffic; here it is flanked on each bank by lush
meadows, cattle and sheep grazing in the downpour. Normally, local children spent their idyllic time poaching here
in an amateurish way or simply enacting some fantasy upon
the waters as children have done since the days of Drake.
It is an area of placid, tranquil wonderland. Dragon and
damselflies spend the summer courting along the surging
flow; kingfishers compete with the haughty heron for the

175

indigenous brown trout; and man stands casting his line, reflecting on days gone by.

Scarback knew this stretch well; she felt refreshed after her two-mile swim and was content to linger awhile among the reeds before attempting the ascent of the pass. Three young grilse joined her, probably her offspring, idly nosing the long green fronds of the rushes. It had become much cooler now.

For twenty-four hours the rain fell, bringing the river into full spate. Scarback could hear the roar of the water as it poured over the weir; the ferocity of the flow was awe-inspiring, and it seemed to be urging the salmon on in their journey up river. The three grilse had already begun to climb the old, worn stone fish-pass, its slimy moss-covered sides speckled with their scales.

Scarback left the comparative stillness of the reeds and swam out once more to mid-stream, receiving the full impact of the flow which momentarily carried her back downstream. But she soon recovered and, with an extra thrust of her powerful tail, headed towards the boiling mass of white water. Her first attempt sent her thrashing back into the heavily charged, oxygenated water; it surprised her, for she had managed twice before to clear it on the very first jump.

Another old-timer had now joined her. She, too, wore the tell-tale signs of UDN (Ulcerative Dermal Necrosis) – the dreaded disease that has plagued the rivers for the past twenty or so years – on her body. Her red lesions also wore the bloom of white fungus.

Scarback watched as she leaped at the surging mass; she also failed and was tossed back. This seemed to encourage Scarback, for she positioned herself in front of the pass, and with a tremendous thrust she not only cleared the narrow gap but rose feet over the crest of the weir, falling back into the quieter, deep water as it surged towards the weir. The terrific smack as she hit the water alerted the river bailiff, who was monitoring the fish count. He was crouched low in the lee of a huge granite overhang. Scarback swam towards him, intending to recover in the reasonably slack water that dribbled off among the copse of willows. Her ruddy livery showed in the clear water. The bailiff made an entry in his notebook. Two mature salmon, hen, eighteen pounds plus, infected UDN.

After a while the effects of the excessive oxygen were beginning to wear off and Scarback once more began to feel a strange tiredness creeping over her. She had seen the outline of the bailiff quite clearly but was too exhausted to dive for cover, so instead she faced the flow, remaining almost stationary. Within minutes she was joined by the other diseased salmon, who seemed to be experiencing the same lassitude.

The sky was now clearing and banks of blue appeared in between the rag-tailed clouds that raced off towards the east. The rain had stopped and there was a distinct drop in the temperature.

An inquisitive heron flew in and waded into the shallows. He watched the two resting fish, not quite able to understand the apparent complete disregard for him shown by the salmon. Towards the cover of sedge grass a cheeky band of daddy-long-legs danced insolently above the head of one of the salmon. Scarback decided she must move on, heading for the quarry where, on her last visit, she had rid herself of the wire snare that had become entangled on her shoulders.

Night had fallen with a clearing sky; every so often the moon would show and cover the ever-moving river in a metallic brightness that hinted of much colder nights ahead. The river had lost much of its thrust, but still surged with a frightening power that carried bulks of flotsam in the flow.

Scarback reached the safety of the quarry just before midnight; the huge chimney and rambling buildings with their rusty tin roofs were like old friends. In this backwater the river, although still swollen, was much quieter being sheltered by woodland. The surface of the water was calm, in fact oily-looking, reflecting the quarry complex on its surface. After the rush of the river and noise of the motorway, all was tranquil, and the moon now shone in a virtually clear sky.

The salmon could be seen searching in the moonlit waters with unhurried ease until she found the old rusty iron stake that leaned crazily towards the wooden wharf. She began to rub herself against it with exaggerated vigour, which only resulted in enlarging the sores, creating a bloody, mucous mass containing several of her scales. It dripped down into the depths, providing temporary interest for a foraging brown trout, who sniffed at the trickle of cloudy blood momentarily before swimming off.

Scarback at last realised that no amount of rubbing was going to rid herself of this irritant; in fact, she began to feel worse after the effort and swam sadly to the refuge of the old boiler that lay submerged just offshore. She spent a fitful night in pain from her damaged body as she listened to the constant calling of an owl in the surrounding woods.

During the early hours of the morning she was joined by several salmon and sea-trout; one she recognised as a fellow sufferer. Somehow the company of the fish seemed to help her in the confused state she was experiencing, although it was only the diseased salmon that sought her immediate company.

The next day brought an easterly wind, and the first hint of winter as the temperature fell several degrees. Scarback entered the main flow once more, where already the river levels were dropping; it was now a race against time to get to her next resting hole until the river rose once more.

Not far behind, her new-found companion was swimming in her wake, as though eager for the comfort of a fellow sufferer. Extreme caution was necessary now as the river became clearer, for Scarback knew this stretch of river to be the haunt of poachers, and she instinctively used the shelter of deep water where possible, remembering not to linger at the next three bridges. There the lads from the neighbouring villages practised all manner of tricks to capture the king of the fish. In company with the other salmon, they cleared the first bridge by noon.

The sun made a feeble effort to cheer, but what warmth it gave was soon lost in the biting east wind, which perhaps accounted for the absence of humans on the banks, though there were always a couple of opportunist youths hanging around the bridge. The water had become bitterly cold towards the afternoon, triggering the salmon's urge to spawn. Scarback swam the length of the river towards Sowton Mill, which was tucked into the hillside; once that was cleared, it wouldn't be very long before she reached the sanctuary near Steppes Bridge.

Two dear ladies lived at the mill whose gardens and grounds were a sheer delight. Here the banks were planted with a diversity of flowers and shrubs, and during high summer the quarter-mile of river was bathed in a profusion of colour and haunting fragrance. Scarback was indeed an old favourite with them the distinctive scar just below her neck made her recognisable during her last visit. She knew that she would be safe along this stretch, but there were two more bridges to pass.

By three o'clock the second bridge was in sight, where the tiny hamlet wanders off into the valley. What Scarback didn't realise was that the infection was damaging her vision, and without warning she headed straight into the gill-net that was stretched cunningly across the pool just under the bridge. In her panic she thrashed around, her weight making a terrific impact in the water that was now getting lower by the hour. However, she was not alone in her captivity; two of the grilse which she had seen earlier at the motorway were also enmeshed, but they gave only a token struggle.

The more Scarback struggled, the tighter the cruel nylon strands bit into her gills until she became gradually weakened by her efforts. Eventually she lay still and twisted, her entire body aching and burning with fever. The salmon that had been following Scarback had somehow sensed that something was amiss and had retreated downstream, searching uneasily for a safe lie. Mercifully, within a short time voices could be heard on the bank and two men began to haul in their illegal harvest. Scarback lay gasping on the bank while she was being released from the treacherous mesh; her head was splitting, and she sensed death was close.

A snarl from the elder of the two men rasped, 'We don't want this horrible bloody, stinking thing – make sure you wash your hands!'

The salmon was roughly tossed back into the river, where she lay on her side, drifting back downstream. She must have travelled at least a quarter of a mile before she managed to summon up enough strength to right her body. Now she was facing the flow and the water passed through her gills, restoring the lost oxygen, but it took most of her efforts to remain on station.

An hour was to pass before she was confident enough to continue her passage towards the bridge, her failing sight causing her to rely much more on her instinct. Her progress was slow, her damaged body adding to her already acute discomfort.

Within yards of the bridge she was joined once more by the escorting salmon, who this time swam alongside Scarback as though wishing to protect her. It was very moving to see the two diseased salmon swimming into the distant, fading light, where already the pole star shone in the darkening sky.

Just one more bridge to pass and then the final stretch to partial safety. The swim through the narrow ribbon of water was darkened by the dense woodland on both banks, and only an early badger and two rabbits saw the passing of the two tired fish as they swam side by side upstream in mutual comfort.

The warm lights of the local bus as it crawled over the stone bridge told Scarback that they were about to pass under the old grey arch. Not a soul was in sight as the bus disappeared into the darkness. It was cold and wintry.

The sliver of moon gave its meagre light grudgingly; as the east wind played a mournful dirge on the telegraph wires, the bridge had been passed without danger. Now for the mill straight.

Both salmon would try, every so often, to shake the invisible burden from their tormented heads, and once they bumped into each other in their futile efforts to rid themselves of this strange predator. Scarback was now deriving comfort from the escorting fish: they both needed each other. And there is nothing really strange in that – after all, we all need love and affection, and the two fish in the throes of their cancerous disease did not want to die alone.

The scent of burning apple wood drifted downstream. Scarback could dimly make out the friendly lights of the mill; the fairy-tale cottage with its four windows lit up and the smoking chimney reassured her that safety was not far away. The fish had no difficulty in making the pass of the low weir, and the smack of the plump bodies echoed through

180

the mill-race, but the resident old tabby barely raised its head before nestling down once more in the open loft window. There was the white flash of the barn owl as it flew out of the barn with barely a glance at the two swimming salmon, heading purposefully towards the distant woods, and from the tiny stone shed the hum of the small turbine sang monotonously to the night air.

Scarback headed steadily upstream; already the river level had fallen considerably, exposing areas of shale and thousands of round pebbles. They made several attempts to navigate these shallows, and at one point she was afraid that there wasn't going to be enough depth of water to reach Holly Pool, where she would be able to rest. Once her companion almost beached herself on one stickle in her determination to pass.

After a while Scarback managed to find a channel of deep water and swam non-stop towards the moor, followed by her escort. It was now possible for them to swim side by side in the bitterly cold water; occasionally they would shake their heads, where the rosettes of cotton-wool fungus could now be seen plainly. As they passed the small meadow, several sheep huddled together for protection, eyeing a furtive fox nervously as it slunk into the hedgerow. Silhouetted in the pale, starry sky, the distant hills, densely covered in oak and beech, offered Scarback her sanctuary – just a few more miles to go.

A shooting star racing across the sky; a barking dog in the distant sleeping village; flashing lights further upstream on the bank, probably poachers on the prowl – all went unnoticed by the tired fish as they neared the pool.

Luck was with them on this night, for the lights were from the bailiffs' lamps as they negotiated a dangerous part of the bank. Both salmon entered Holly Pool just as dawn was showing through the trees. The banks glistened with the first frost of winter. Two lumbering badgers were homeward bound after a night's foraging, their wet noses enveloped in tiny vapour clouds as they climbed the steep hillside. A solitary duck paddled towards Scarback as she settled beneath the gnarled, mossy roots of the oak; her mate had gone off in search of a similar refuge.

For the next few days the entire countryside was wreathed in thick mist and gripped by frost, with the river down to a low flow. There was not enough water to make the weir at the bridge; Scarback had made two attempts to reach it, but each time was stopped yards from the fish-pass. The river barely covered the pebbled bottom under the bridge, and it was impossible for her to swim. She retreated once more into her cavern to await the next spate; her strength ebbed daily and the whole of her back was now covered in sores. Even if the rains came, would she have enough strength to make the pass?

Her entire body was on fire, and the urge to spawn was becoming unbearable; somehow she must make her 'redd' in the pebbles under the bridge, although the last time she had spawned much further up past Fingles. The escorting salmon had not been seen since they had both arrived at the pool. Scarback's sight was failing fast; each morning the ruddy, frosty dawn appeared as a crimson smudge, and she wondered how much longer she could endure this agony.

On the seventh morning, in sunlit frost, she edged cautiously towards the pebbles. She knew that once her eggs were laid and she was able to reach the sea, the salt water would cure her of the infection. In the bitter cold morning she began to excavate her redd, although so far no cock salmon was in attendance to fertilise the eggs. It took her some time to deposit at least half of her orange pearls; she was completely exhausted.

That night the growing moon soaked the entire valley in a beautiful soft sheen as Scarback made her way back to her resting place. The channel in which she had travelled upstream to the bridge had, during the day, become shallower. She was unable to reach her cavern. As she tried to turn herself she became wedged in the oozing, gravelled bed and barely half her body was covered with water.

The moon shone down on her ravaged body. This once noble fish who had left this very river of her birth and had journeyed far across the Atlantic, now lay stranded in the shadow of the tree-covered hills. A single owl called from the dark silence of the wood. Once again, the badgers came down from the hillside to forage, and a bedraggled vixen even passed within feet of Scarback, failing to see or smell her presence as she loped off into the undergrowth.

Scarback, through film-covered eyes, could see the pole star shining high in the sky, remembering it as an old friend during her sea voyages. Unknown to her, not yards away, wedged in another shallow, her escort lay already dead.

That morning the crimson sun bathed the river in an orange glow. The frost began to thaw, dripping from the overhanging branches, and a robin sang to the new day. Further upstream two large, sinister crows were disputing the ownership of a salmon who lay on her side. Scarback lay staring up at the sky with eyeless sockets.

'. . . all that lives must die,
passing through nature to eternity.'
William Shakespeare, *Hamlet* I. ii